D1233579

Exploring with Your Microscope

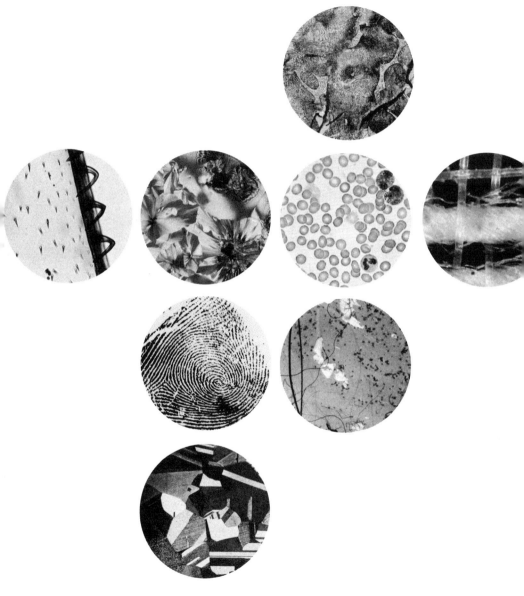

Julian D. Corrington

Professor of Zoology, University of Miami

EXPLORING

WITH YOUR

MICROSCOPE

New York   Toronto   London

McGRAW-HILL BOOK COMPANY, INC.

Fourth Printing

13179

Published by the McGraw-Hill Book Company, Inc.

Printed in the United States of America

Preface

An earlier book by the author of this volume has been out of print for a number of years. This was *Adventures with the Microscope,* published by the Bausch & Lomb Optical Company in 1934. After the lapse of a generation, it was judged that an abridged and revised work, following somewhat the general plan of the older book, would be in order. Some of the material and illustrations have been taken from a second volume, *Working with the Microscope* (McGraw-Hill Book Company, Inc., 1941), a strictly technical manual, but the bulk of the present volume is new. Its scope and purpose are described in Chapter 1.

We have been greatly aided by several of the major optical companies—American Optical, Bausch & Lomb, and E. Leitz, and by other manufacturers and dealers. Our thanks go to them for furnishing specially posed and new illustrations. The photomicrographs are the work of John V. Butterfield, F.B.P.A., and their quality explains the esteem in which he is held by colleagues in his specialized profession. The slides that were photographed were kindly lent by Ward's Natural Science Establishment.

The line drawings are the work of the author's wife, Veronica E. Corrington, who obligingly put aside her water-color brushes for a summer in order to turn out these lively and essential aids to the text.

Julian D. Corrington

Contents

chapter one

Amateur microscopy

In the various arts and sciences pursued by mankind there are generally more amateurs than professionals. If we use the word *amateur* in its correct sense, as one who follows a study for the love of it and not as a means of earning a living, it is clear that this word does not indicate a beginner, still less an incompetent worker. There have been many celebrated amateur painters, singers, and scientists of all sorts, including microscopists.

This book has been written for you who take up microscopy as a hobby or avocation. Of the numerous hobbies, some trivial, some serious, none is so comprehensive as microscopy, since this study leads into every field of science and to many of the arts and industries as well. As you go through the various chapters that follow, you will find that the microscope is indeed the king of scientific instruments, and if you learn to understand it and use it properly, you will open up inexhaustible sources of pleasure as well as the opportunity to go as far as you wish along any of the many pathways in science.

What is microscopy?

Microscopy (mī-krŏs′-kō-pī) embraces the art and the science of using the microscope; one who follows this work is a *microscopist* (mī-krŏs′-kō-pĭst). In practice, microscopy is not a separate science itself but an aspect of other sciences. Thus a microscopist thinks of himself primarily as an entomologist, a botanist, or a geologist. The microscope is a means to an end rather than an end in itself. Nevertheless there is a certain amount of basic information about this instrument and its uses that you should know if you are engaged in any branch of science. You should know the parts of the microscope, what they do, and how to adjust and care for this expensive appliance. You should know the kinds of microscopes, how to set up the right sort of illumination for each, and something about the many accessories that are available for special purposes. Above all you should know how to prepare the endless array of subjects for examination under the microscope; this knowledge is indicated by the term *micrology* (mī-krŏl′-ō-jĭ) or, more commonly, *microtechnique*.

Once you have gained some information and experience in manipulating the instrument and in preparing a representative series of microscope slides—what then? In some hobbies the operator never gets beyond the collecting stage. It may be stamps or coins or butterflies—they are collected and arranged, and there the interest in them ceases, pride in numbers and kinds and in ownership being satisfied. But the serious worker wants to know more, often much more, about his specimens. A collection of microscope slides is valueless for mere display purposes. Some, such as a slide showing a skillfully arranged group of diatoms, may represent the ultimate in the art of mounting and the craftsman may take justifiable pride in his abilities, but the real purpose behind this achievement is to be able to study diatoms.

Let us imagine that you as a beginner have made your first sections of a plant leaf. They may be crudely cut and poorly stained, but they are of your own manufacture and you think they are wonderful. Soon your technique improves and you begin to observe more and more about what the slide exhibits and to think a bit less about the merely mechanical preparation. What are all these objects seen in a cross section of a leaf? What do they do for the plant? Once this sort of question gains the upper hand over technique, you have taken the second step in microscopy. You hunt up a textbook on botany and find that you have discovered palisade cells and that these and their neighbors are the basic factories for all the food of the world. Without these cells there would be no agriculture, no commerce, no people! This is an amazing thought, but only the beginning as you develop from an embryo technician and start becoming an amateur botanist.

Sampling the field

Unless you are already well versed in certain specialties or committed to some definite career, you would do well to make a trial excursion into many fields before settling upon one. How do you know what will prove to be of greatest interest until you try several? One person may prefer to go in for insects, another for textiles. Our advice is, then, to make a number of observations and slide preparations in each of the departments that follow. Find out how the microscope is used in chemistry, physics, zoology, bacteriology, and other sciences, or in soil surveying, metallurgy, photoengraving, and other applied and industrial uses. After completing this orientation, there is usually nothing to be gained by continuing to generalize. If histology (microscopic anatomy) appeals to you as most interesting, consider that subject as the main one for your further activities with the microscope. Get a good modern textbook of histology and a technique manual, and with them study the whole area of histology for a year or more. Finally, specialize still further by picking out some subdivision of this science, such as the blood cells, and devote the bulk of your study time to the mastery of this more limited field. Someone else may care little for histology but find great appeal in scientific crime detection, an applied specialty that uses many kinds of optical instruments. In this manner you become proficient.

The purpose of this book, then, is to introduce you to some of the main sciences, and show how the microscope is employed in them and how a few of the slide preparations for each are made. The book should serve both the amateur working alone, who needs a guide to direct his efforts and the high school and college student, in the elements of various sciences. A textbook of biology, for example, tells quite a bit about microscopic animals but seldom anything about the microscope and never anything on how to prepare these animals for study; there simply is not time in the course or space in the book to do so for all the many groups of plants and animals.

Another thing that you as a beginning amateur can do to further your progress is to subscribe to one or more periodicals, some of which are listed here, and to join a microscope society or club. There may be a local club in your home town or high school or college. By joining it you will meet others with similar interests.

Periodicals dealing with or including a department of microscopy

American Microscopical Society, *Transactions*, 50 E. Broad St., Columbus, Ohio. Quarterly, $8 per year. Technical, advanced, professional.

Microscope, The, British journal of microscopy, photomicrography, and entomology. Bimonthly, $3 per year. American agent: Harry Ross, 61 Reade St., New York 7, N.Y. Suitable for the average amateur.

Nature Magazine, published ten times per year by The American Nature Association, 1214 Sixteenth St., N.W., Washington 6, D.C. $5 per year; foreign $5.50. Includes a department on amateur microscopy.

Scientific American, 415 Madison Ave., New York 17, N.Y. Monthly, $5 per year. Includes a department, "The Amateur Scientist," which often contains material on microscopy. Popular.

Stain Technology, a journal for microtechnic (Biological Stain Commission). Quarterly, $4.50 per year. Biotech Publications, Geneva, N.Y. Suitable for advanced amateurs.

chapter two

Concerning microscopes

What is a microscope? The word comes from two Greek roots —*micros*, small, and *scopos*, a watcher—and signifies an instrument through which one observes small things. Magnification is not implied in the word itself, but in using the term "microscope" magnification is always implied.

Now in order to increase the apparent size of an object we must bring it up to the eye to examine it more closely. People generally hold things they wish to inspect carefully 10 in. from the eye; at this distance the eye focuses accurately. Most people can still see the object in sharp detail when it is held 6 in. away from the face, but when it is brought ever closer a point is reached at which the vision blurs and we can no longer discern the material clearly. The object appears much larger, it is true, but we have here an instance of *magnification without resolution*—enlargement without the possibility of distinguishing detail. This is empty, valueless magnification. If there were some way to get the eye close to the work, say 1 in. from it, and still see full details in sharp focus, we should be able to observe finer structure than befote; this would be true magnification with suitable accompanying resolution—a bug's-eye view, so to speak.

How big is the moon? Astronomers tell us that our satellite is 2,162 miles in diameter, but to the inexperienced child it seems about the size of a dinner plate. We can hold a dime in front of the eye in such a way as to mask the view of the full moon, but we are all aware that the dime and the moon are not thereby equal in diameter. Size depends on distance; anything seen at less than 10 in. is enlarged, which is to say magnified. In the Middle Ages it was discovered that by shaping a piece of glass into curved surfaces—making a lens—and then examining an object through this lens, it was possible to get the eye very close indeed to the material and behold much finer detail than the human eye had ever before witnessed. Thus arose first the simple and later the compound microscope.

A *lens*, named from its shape (from the Latin for "lentil," which has the contour of a biconvex disk), is able to show us such detail because of the way it affects the rays of light it transmits. Light will pass through a sheet of glass having parallel sides, like a window pane, without suffering *deviation*, i.e., without being bent. But the two curved surfaces of a lens are not parallel. The velocity of light is slowed up in going through so dense a material as glass, and the rays bend so as to take the shortest route through, the pathway requiring the least time (a principle discovered by a French mathematician, Pierre Fermat, in the seventeenth century). The visible effect is *refraction* (bending) of the rays. If the lens is properly shaped, these rays can be made to converge to a point known as the *focus* and then go on to form an image beyond. Every point in the object is reproduced by a conjugate point in the image. If we place our eye at a suitable distance from the focal point, we will perceive this image, and it is possible to grind lenses with shorter and shorter focal distances so that we get the eye closer and closer to the object and still see its image in sharp clarity. By an artificial means, then, we improve on nature and render the eye capable of viewing objects at extremely short distances, thus observing them in ever greater detail, as if we could constantly reduce our size and get continually closer, obtaining a mouse's-eye view, then a bug's-eye view, and then a microbe's-eye view.

Any appliance that enables us to improve on nature in this way is, technically, a *microscope*. The oldest form is owned by a large number of people, who carry them about on their noses—for spectacles are simple microscopes, though we do not refer to them as such. They provide a small amount of magnification, in most cases, and many also correct visual defects. Reading glasses, telescopes, and opera or field glasses are other types of microscopes that are not ordinarily so called. In practice we restrict the word to those instruments that have a short focal distance and are customarily placed close to relatively small objects, or small areas of larger ones, for the purpose of giving us magnified views.

When the word microscope is mentioned, the kind that comes to mind is the *laboratory* or *biological compound microscope* (Fig. 1.) Doubtless most people think of this instrument as the only form of microscope; it certainly is the most numerous and important, though only one of many varieties today. Likewise the average person would expect to find these microscopes solely in school laboratories, doctors' offices, and hospitals. The general impression seems to be that microscopes play an inconspicuous and relatively minor role in our daily lives, but we shall show that the microscope is the basic tool of modern scientific and industrial research and is beyond question the king of instruments. In a very real sense our civilization is founded on microscopes. The food we eat, the fluids we drink, the clothes we wear, the metals we use, the raw materials of the basic industries, and all the thousands of manufactured articles that make up the gadgetry of our complex civilization—all pass at some stage under a microscope and are scrutinized for purity, ingredients, particle sizes, uniformity, and other important aspects. Indeed the microscope is worth knowing.

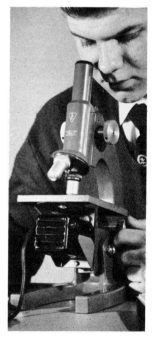

Fig. 1. *Biological compound microscope, with double nosepiece and without condenser. Substage lamp in place of mirror. (Courtesy Bausch & Lomb.)*

Parts of the compound microscope

There are many separate parts in a compound microscope, but all of them fall into one or the other of two categories— the optical and the mechanical. The *optical parts* are the essential ones for producing enlarged images; the *mechanical parts* are necessary ones that make it possible to place the object in suitable relation to the optical parts and to manipulate these optical parts easily and conveniently. Refer to Figure 2 while studying the following description, and also to your own microscope, carrying out the various suggestions wherever possible.

MECHANICAL PARTS The foundation upon which the microscope rests is the *base*, from which the *pillar* rises to support the entire instrument. These two parts are a single unit, cast in one piece. It must be heavy so as to provide stability, making it difficult to knock over the microscope. Turn your instrument upside down so as to inspect the base, first removing the eyepiece and placing it to one side; otherwise, being free, it could fall out and be damaged. Note that the microscope actually rests upon three small areas, two toes and a heel, the principle of the tripod, the most perfect form of support. Restore the instrument to its normal position and replace the eyepiece.

At the top of the pillar is the *inclination joint*, which permits tilting the microscope from the vertical to the horizontal, and above this comes the *stage*, upon which the material to be examined is placed. An *aperture* in the center of the stage admits light from below, and two *spring clips* serve to hold a microscope slide in place. The aperture must be situated on the *optical axis* of the instrument. This is a straight line— that which would be traversed by an axial light ray—reflected by the mirror so as to pass upward through the exact center of all the optical parts.

Everything that lies below the stage comprises the *substage*. In less expensive models the substage includes the mirror assembly, diaphragm, and filter holder. The *mirror assembly* consists of the *mirror* itself, usually plane on one surface and concave on the other, and the *mirror fork*, which allows rotation in the horizontal plane, so that surfaces of the mirror can be changed and so that the mirror can be set at the desired angle. This fork may plug into the pillar so as to provide rotation in the vertical plane; the combination of the horizontal and vertical movements makes it possible to adjust the angle of the mirror in any position. Removal of the mirror is necessary for the use of certain types of microscope illumi-

8

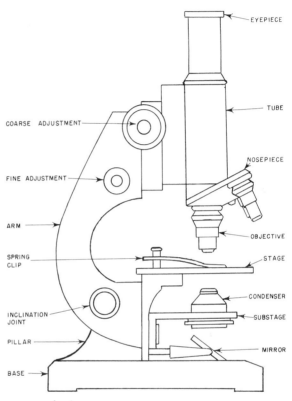

Fig. 2. Parts of the compound microscope.

nants. Sometimes the fork is held by a *mirror arm,* swiveled to the pillar to move in pendulum fashion, in which case the mirror can be moved to the side, out of the optical axis, and thus deliver oblique light.

Attached to the underside of the stage is the diaphragm, which may be in either of two forms. The *disk diaphragm* is a wheel, an edge of which projects just beyond the front stage margin, so that it may be revolved with a fingertip. With a click it comes to a stop; any of several sizes of apertures comes to rest aligned with the stage aperture, controlling the diameter of the shaft of light admitted from the mirror below. The *iris diaphragm* does the same thing, but by continuous graduation of sizes, as the thin metal leaves mesh; it is like the same item in a camera, where it is familiar to many who have never examined a microscope. Usually there is a swing-out ring beneath the diaphragm in which can be seated any of several kinds of *filter disks*—made of ground glass or blue glass, for most purposes.

In the more expensive or elaborate models, a small separate microscope called the *condenser* is situated above the mirror; its purpose is to focus the incoming light rays. It is essential for use with the highest-powered of the optical parts—the oil-immersion objective. The iris diaphragm and filter holder assembly are attached to the bottom of the condenser. Since it is necessary to focus the condenser, it moves up or down by means of a rack-and-pinion gear; it may swing out or unplug for cleaning or adjusting.

Rising above the stage from the inclination joint is the *arm*. In most models this part is curved to bring the optical parts forward over the stage aperture and at the same time form a convenient hand grip by which the microscope is carried. The arm supports the *body tube*, which bears the optics at each end. Sometimes there is a second tube within the first, the *draw tube,* which pulls out like a section of a spyglass, increasing the magnification along with the length of the main tube. The body tube moves up and down for focusing; this essential motion is performed by turning either of two pairs (sometimes only one pair) of wheels with milled edges—the coarse and fine adjustment heads. The larger of the two is the *coarse adjustment head,* actuating a rack-and-pinion gear.

To see how the coarse adjustment works, remove the eyepiece, grasp the body tube with the palm of the right hand, and, assisting by turning the left coarse adjustment head clockwise with the left hand, pull straight up, slowly and gently, disengaging the tube completely. That part of the microscope remaining, divested of the tube, is the *stand;* face this around and inspect the *pinion gear,* a spiral series of cogs. These engage the slots between the teeth of the *rack,* which is screwed to the rear of the body tube. This device is an example of a simple machine and constitutes one of a series of great inventions by medieval man in the field of mechanics, a division of physics. The rack-and-pinion gear permits change of motion from rotary to vertical; it is a modification of the principle of the inclined plane. In replacing the tube, start carefully and mesh the gears, then turn the coarse adjustment head so as to lower the tube. Do not use force. Movement of this head is commonly referred to as "racking the tube up (or down)." Always replace the eyepiece in the tube promptly to prevent dust from falling upon the parts at the bottom of the tube.

The *fine adjustment heads* are the smaller of the two pairs; they rack the tube up and down very slowly and over very brief intervals. There are several types of actuating mechanisms; some use cams, others micrometer screws, rollers, ball bearings. No one but a factory-trained expert should ever tamper with or attempt to repair this adjustment. In many models, the right head is also a *micrometer head,* since it is equipped with a scale to permit measurements in depth of objects on the stage. Older microscopes may have a single horizontal head at the top of the arm, while the newest models feature two heads so low on the microscope as to be located on the pillar, where they may be operated while the hand rests on the table, a design that adds to comfort. Being an expensive part, the fine adjustment is omitted on some microscopes. A recent American Optical student microscope has a single gear, intermediate in ratio between standard coarse and standard fine.

OPTICAL PARTS   There are three essential components in any observation with a microscope—the object, the microscope, and the observer. In recognition of this triple alliance, the optical part nearest the object is called the *objective*, and that nearest the observer's eyes is the *eyepiece*, or *ocular*.

Remove the eyepiece, at the upper end of the tube, and note that it consists of a polished barrel surmounted by a flange to prevent the piece from falling down the tube. Unscrew and remove this flange, which supports the *eye lens;* likewise remove the similar element at the bottom of the barrel—the *field lens*. Both are planoconvex lenses, i.e., one surface of the single piece of glass is flat, the other convex.

In both, the convex surface faces the object; this arrangement is referred to as *Huygenian* (hī-gē'-nĭ-ăn), since it was invented by a great optical scientist, Christiaan Huygens (hī'-gĕnz) in the seventeenth century.

Observe that there is a platform inside the barrel, the *eye-piece diaphragm*. This serves to reduce the size of the field of view seen through the microscope and sharpens the image by cutting off the marginal rays of light, which have a habit of coming to a focus at a different plane from that of the central rays. This diaphragm is also most useful because the microscopist can place various items upon it and they will appear to lie in the image scanned through the instrument. Thus, we may fasten a hair on this diaphragm in such a way that the tip seems to lie in the tissue being inspected and therefore can be used as a pointer in teaching or in showing someone else what you wish him to see (page 48). Or we may put a ruled scale on this diaphragm, and the scale will seem to lie in the field and so permit direct measurements. The four powers of Huygenian oculars most commonly seen are the 5×, 7.5×, 10×, and 15×. If only one is to be had, it should be the 7.5×; if two are furnished with your microscope, they are no doubt the 5× and 10×. The symbol × here means "times," indicating magnification. Reassemble the parts of the eyepiece.

The objective (Fig. 3) is more complex. Many kinds are manufactured. The principal ones, in terms of the medium lying between the cover glass of the slide and the objectives, are dry, water-immersion, glycerin-immersion, and oil-immersion. Referring to degree of correction of defects, there are achromatic and apochromatic objectives; referring to composition of the refracting substances, there are glass, fluorite, and quartz objectives; and of course these types are made in several degrees of magnifying power. Of these many possible combinations, the three objectives found on the great majority of biological microscopes today will be glass achromatics known as the low-dry, the high-dry, and the oil-immersion.

The *low-power dry objective* magnifies 10×. It is the shortest one of the three, coming to a focus at a considerable elevation above the object. Another way of stating this is to say that it has a long *working distance,* which is the space between the cover glass or object (if uncovered) and the bottom of the objective. Commonly this objective is *divisible.* Unscrew this objective from the microscope and then unscrew the bottom half (the *front combination*) if the barrel is marked "divisible." Inspect both portions, noting that each has an optical part. What appears to be a single lens in each is actually a union of two lenses cemented together to act as one, the lower in each case being planoconcave, the upper biconvex. Each separate lens is a *component;* a combination of two cemented lenses is a *doublet.* The doublet, since it acts as a unit in producing an image but is not the entire objective, is an *element.* Unfortunately the term lens has been applied to any or all of these: to the single piece of glass, the doublet or other element, to a triplet (three cemented lenses), and to the whole objective, so that its meaning has become vague. Screw the base, or *rear combination,* back onto the microscope; when used alone this is a 32-mm. objective. The magnification is only 4×; this is important to remember since one often wishes this low a power in looking at relatively large objects. The fact that this objective is divisible adds another objective to your equipment. Screw the front combination back upon the rear one.

The *high-dry objective* magnifies 43×, or some figure close to this, depending upon make and model. It is not divisible and should never be taken apart by anyone save a trained factory worker. Reference to Figure 3 will show that the elements are

Fig. 3. Sectional views of objectives, showing construction. Left: *10×, with 2 elements of 2 lenses each; center, 43×, 3 elements, lenses 2–2–1; right: 97×, 4 elements, lenses 2–2–1–1. (Courtesy American Optical Co.) ·*

all at the bottom of this and the oil-immersion objectives and that they are held in *cells* that are very skillfully machined and adjusted. Obviously if one of these high-priced parts is dropped or banged against some hard substance, the objective may be seriously damaged. The *oil-immersion objective,* found only on advanced models, magnifies 97× or thereabouts, and is the most costly single item of the microscope.

These objectives are supported by a *nosepiece,* actually a mechanical part of the instrument but considered here for convenience. Nosepieces are double, triple, quadruple, etc., according to the number carried. Biological microscopes in the lower price bracket have a double nosepiece for two objectives, the 10× and 43×, while in the higher price range the nosepiece is triple, with objectives 10×, 43×, and oil-immersion 97×. Operate the nosepiece, noting that as it revolves it brings each objective successively into the optical axis, the correct alignment being announced by a click, as the *detent* engages a slight notch. Another service of the nosepiece is to protect the interior of the objectives from dust at all times. This function accounts for the shape of the nosepiece.

When the microscope is set up for use and focused on a specimen, the objective components, acting as a single lens, in that one final image results, form a *real image* of the object at the level of the eyepiece diaphragm (Fig. 4). This image is so called because it has a real existence, independent of the human eye. With the eye lens removed and the barrel of the eyepiece secured in place by Scotch Tape, a piece of tissue paper may be cut as a disk to fit upon the platform of the diaphragm; when the room is dark and proper illumination of the object is employed, the image will be seen upon this paper—or upon tobacco smoke blown into the tube. A real image is inverted and reversed; it may be projected or photographed. In the Huygenian ocular, the field lens acts with the objective, and the real image is formed between the two eyepiece lenses, a design called a *negative ocular.* By comparison, the *Ramsden ocular* is a *positive* one, the image formed below both lenses. In the Ramsden, the two convex surfaces face each other. Such an eyepiece is used in micrometry and in corrected forms for research equipment.

The observer looks at the real image through the eye lens,

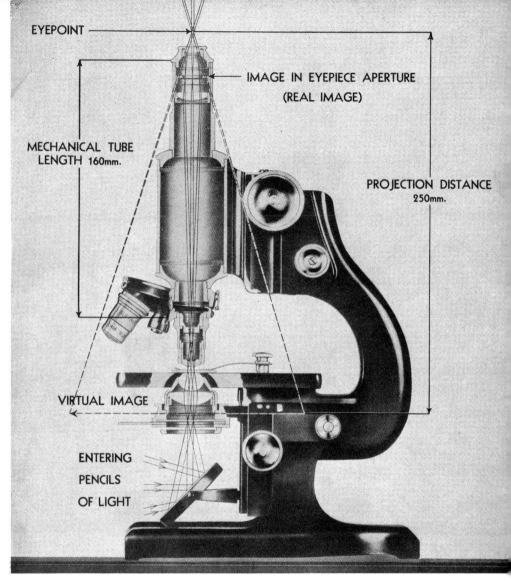

EYEPOINT

IMAGE IN EYEPIECE APERTURE
(REAL IMAGE)

MECHANICAL TUBE
LENGTH 160mm.

PROJECTION DISTANCE
250mm.

VIRTUAL IMAGE

ENTERING
PENCILS
OF LIGHT

which acts as a simple magnifier or hand lens, and sees this real image remagnified and as a *virtual image*, the apparent location being in a plane below the stage of the microscope, 10 in. from the *eyepoint*, above the ocular, where the eye is placed (Fig. 4). This virtual image is erect, has no real existence, and cannot be either projected or photographed. We think we are looking down the tube at the object itself, but that

Fig. 4. Path of light rays through a compound microscope; formation of images. (Courtesy American Optical Co.)

is not the case at all. We are actually scanning an image of the object instead of the real thing, a small real image located at about the end of our nose, and we are mentally projecting that image, enlarged to occupy a circle about 6 in. in diameter and 10 in. distant, out into space. There is no such image present at that place, but it is none the less evident to the observer. The cooperation of the human eye and mind are necessary in producing virtual images, which are actually a form of optical illusion.

The magnifying power stated for the various objectives is termed the *initial magnification* and denotes the degree of enlargement of the real image over the original object. When this is multiplied by the stated power of the eyepiece, the *final magnification,* which is the degree of enlargement of the virtual image over the original object, is achieved. Thus, if we are using the $10\times$ objective and $10\times$ eyepiece, the final magnification is $100\times$; if now we change to the high-dry, $43\times$ objective, the image we see will be enlarged $430\times$. Magnifications are always stated in diameters, never in areas. If we augment the length 100 times we are also enlarging the breadth by a factor of 100, but to say that we have a magnification of 10,000 would be completely misleading.

How microscopes magnify

We have seen that magnification consists in getting the eye closer to the work. The simplest device for this purpose (and therefore the simplest form of microscope) is the pinhole card, and its use is very instructive for several purposes. Cut a piece of black photo-mount card about 3 by 6 in., and in the center of one end—1½ in. from each of three edges—puncture a tiny hole with a fine needle. As an object, select a colored advertisement in a magazine. Look at this first with the unaided eye at the 10-in. distance, designated in optics as the *near point.* Bring the picture closer to the eye, noting that at some distance, usually less than 6 in., but varying widely with different persons, the details blur. Now look at the picture through the pinhole of the card, with a strong light shining from behind your head, directed upon the picture. You will find that the illustration can now be brought to within 2 in. or even as close as 1 in. from your eye and you will still see a clear picture. This is because only a few axial rays of light are being employed and there is no host of marginal rays to cause glare and drown out detail. Our observation explains one reason for the use of diaphragms (also called *stops*) in optical equipment, such as the eyepiece diaphragm.

But something else has occurred. You will now see the dots of several colors which make up the picture. A line, such as that forming a person's nose, will no longer appear as a continuous line, but as a series of dots; the pinhole card allows the observer to *resolve* the color-process screens used in reproducing the picture. You are actually getting a bug's-eye view of the page, and, if your eye is 1 in. from the object, the magnification is in the ratio of 1:10 in., or 10×. It is possible to achieve this astounding result without a lens!

We can look at postage stamps and similar flat objects with the pinhole card, but we are hindered by difficulties of illumination and eyelashes and cannot get closer to the work than about 1 in. If we make the hole larger, to admit more light, glare destroys the image. The next step is to do as was done by Antonj van Leeuwenhoek (Lā'-vĕn-hook), famous Dutch amateur microscopist of Delft, 1632–1723. He placed a very small, almost spherical lens in a metal frame, something like a pinhole card, and, with the best of such simple microscopes, obtained a magnification of 300×. Figure 5 demonstrates what this does for the eye. In *A*, the observer is looking at the object with the unaided eye. The angle made with the eye by the two extreme points on the object is the *visual angle*, and as long as this is equal to or greater than one minute of arc, we shall see the two marginal points as two and not as one; we can *resolve* the limits of the object. Reference to the figure will show that a larger visual angle would subtend a bigger object or, conversely, if the limits of the object are too close together we shall see only a single point and no detail at all.

If now we place a lens between the object and the eye (Fig. 5*B*), the incident rays of light coming from the object are refracted into a focal point, giving a much wider visual angle. A real image is thrown upon the retina of the eye, but this is not what is "seen" in the mind. Instead, the mind interprets this increased visual angle at its face value and projects the

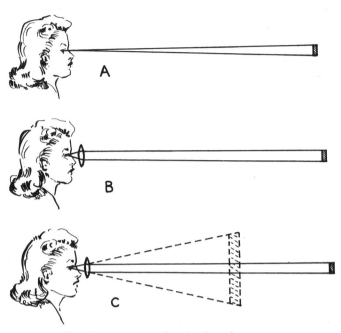

Fig. 5. A lens increases the visual angle.

lines of the refracted rays out into space to the 10-in. near point, and we think we see an erect image of the object at that level (Fig. 5*C*). All observations through lenses, whether in microscopes, telescopes, spectroscopes, or binocular field glasses, are virtual images formed in this manner. Magnification, then, consists in getting the eye closer to the work, and this is done by increasing the visual angle by means of a lens.

Kinds of microscopes

So many different kinds of microscopes have appeared in recent years that even a classification of them is difficult. The one we have been describing uses ordinary light as the means for image formation and so is designated a light microscope, to contrast with those designed for some other form of radiant energy, such as ultraviolet, X rays, and electron beams. Even among microscopes employing visible light we can so alter the rays as to produce very different effects for special purposes, and thus we have dark-field, polarized-light, phase-contrast, and interferometer optics. Further, microscopes may be either

18

refracting or reflecting; this is true also of telescopes. Among light microscopes the primary division is into simple and compound.

No one knows for certain just when microscopes were invented. That the simple form came first is obvious from the fact that the eye lens alone of a compound microscope is a simple microscope. At times there have been attempts to show that the ancients possessed a knowledge of the principles of magnification and means of obtaining it, but the several alleged cases of magnification cited to prove such statements all break down when critically examined, and it is generally believed that Roger Bacon (1214–1294), English monk, philosopher, and scientist, was the first to make spectacles. In the ensuing centuries lens grinding and spectacle making and vending became recognized trades.

The first hand magnifiers were called flea glasses (*vitrea pulicaria*) or fly glasses (*vitrea muscaria*), terms that call attention to the uses to which these simple microscopes were put. They were metal tubes with a lens at the viewing end and were mostly about the size of one's thumb. It is a sad commentary on the state of learning in the Middle Ages that, possessed of these implements for exploring the unknown world of the very small, men could see no use for these toys but that of inspecting each other's external parasites. Microscopes were fads for some three hundred years. The state of personal hygiene, or rather its lack, is also indicated by this fact; it was anticipated that men, like animals, would harbor an external fauna! As with cigarette lighters today, there were simple bronze flea glasses for the ordinary mortal, silver ones for the well-to-do, and gold, often embossed and encrusted with jewels, for the noble or wealthy.

The climax of development of the simple microscope was attained by Leeuwenhoek in the seventeenth century. Using diamond dust, then easily obtained as a waste from the gem-cutting trade, he ground and polished his own lenses. He believed that the simple microscope would always prove superior to the compound. With a tiny lens mounted in a curious frame (Fig. 6), this relatively uneducated man opened up the whole world of the invisible, discovering bacteria, protozoa, and a host of other minute organisms or parts of larger ones.

Fig. 6. Leeuwenhoek's microscope, viewed from the front.

SIMPLE MICROSCOPES   A simple *microscope* may have one or more lenses, but they are so designed and framed as to produce a single, erect, virtual image. The commonest example is the pocket magnifier, or hand lens, but the many different requirements of the various trades and arts have brought a multitude of variations on the main theme (Fig. 7). Those marked

Fig. 7. Many kinds of simple microscopes. (Courtesy Bausch & Lomb.)

1 in the figure are *folding pocket magnifiers,* 2 is a *reader,* 3 a *tripod magnifier,* widely used in elementary biology, 4 is a *linen tester,* 5 an *adjustable-stand magnifier,* 6 a *utility magnifier,* 7 a *double-lens magnifier,* and those in 8 are *loupes.* The linen tester folds flat for the pocket; when opened, it is always in focus, and the field is 1 sq. in. Originally designed for counting the number of threads per square inch in textiles, it finds many other uses today. The utility magnifier is the instrument of choice, among simple microscopes, to inspect fingerprints, postage stamps, photoengravings, and other flat objects. Loupes are held in the bony socket of the eyeball and stem originally from the watchmaker's trade. They are made in different powers and with or without a headband. Still other models are shaped like a fountain pen, with a pocket clip; some of these are simple, some are compound, and some have their own self-contained source of illumination in the form of battery and bulb, like a pocket flashlight. The eyepiece of your compound microscope will serve as a hand lens if held upside down.

Magnifications furnished by simple microscopes range from $2\times$ to $20\times$, though anything over $10\times$ is unusual; mostly they are about $4\times$. Some consist of a single lens, others are doublets or triplets. Prices vary from $1 to $15 or more. The buyer is justified in asking the cause for this range—and this brings us to consider certain defects known as *aberrations* that are inherent in all simple lenses. Of the numerous defects, the two most important to understand are spherical aberration and chromatic aberration.

If parallel rays of light, as from the sun, enter a biconvex lens, they should theoretically all be refracted to meet at a single point, the focus (Fig. 8), but only a lens whose radius of curvature varies continually from center to edge could do that, and such a surface cannot be ground mechanically. What actually happens in lenses whose surfaces are segments of spheres is that the marginal rays are bent in more sharply than are the central ones and meet at a focal point (f^m, Fig. 9) apart from that of the central rays (f^c). Light rays in between marginal and central come to a focus at varying intermediate points. The result is that instead of a single, sharp, focal plane, giving a flat field of view with everything clearly in focus, the

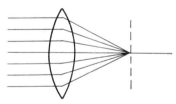

Fig. 8. Theoretical focus of biconvex lens.

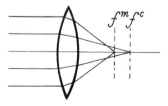

Fig. 9. Actual focus with a biconvex lens. Fm—focal point for marginal rays; Fc—focal point for central rays.

focus is spread out over an area of depth, and the image may be sharp at the center while fuzzy at the margins, or vice versa, or it may be gray, lacking in contrast, or it may show *pincushion distortion*, in which straight lines curve toward the center, or *barrel distortion*, in which they curve away from the center, depending upon a variety of factors. This is *spherical aberration*.

Further, when white light, such as that from the sun, enters glass obliquely, it suffers *dispersion* along with refraction—a fanning out into a rainbow of all the colors of the spectrum. This is because white light is composed of waves of radiant energy of many different lengths, and the velocity of each is retarded differently in glass, so that the angle of refraction of each is different. The effect is that the reds and oranges at the lower end of the spectrum (longer wavelengths) are refracted less and meet at a focal point (f^c, Fig. 9) farther from the lens than do the blue and violet waves that are bent in more sharply (f^m). This is *chromatic aberration*, a defect that produces fringes and halos of color in the image.

Correction of defects may take any of several forms, but the product is invariably more expensive than a simple, uncorrected lens. An element or objective corrected for spherical aberration is said to be *aplanatic;* one corrected for chromatic aberration is *achromatic*. In simple microscopes, a *cemented doublet* may be constructed of two lenses, the first a biconvex component of *crown glass*, an alkali-lime type, and the second a diverging meniscus component of *flint glass*, a heavy type containing lead. A *meniscus* lens is crescent-shaped, concave on one surface and convex on the other. If its edges are thicker than its center, it diverges light rays; if the center is the thicker, it converges. The chemical formula for each of these kinds of glass can be so selected as to correct most of both the spherical and the chromatic aberrations; the first lens magnifies and disperses the *incident rays* (entering rays), the second minifies and recombines the rays with such a total effect that there will still be some magnifying power left while the light will again appear white. Through custom the term achromatic has come to include aplanatic in descriptions of objectives. This is logical since the same methods correct both defects together, and a single word is needed. The degree of correction is partial. The finest of all objectives, with the greatest degree of correction, are termed *apochromatic*. They require *compensating eyepieces* and are used for research and photomicrography.

A *cemented triplet* is the finest type of simple magnifier; it is classed as "highly corrected." The *Coddington magnifier* is a single block of glass with a groove diaphragm cut in its middle; this ingenious invention gives moderate correction. *Spaced doublets* and *triplets* achieve limited correction (semiaplanatic, semiachromatic). There is thus a style, power, and price for every need and purse. Every microscopist should own at least one simple microscope as a supplement to his other equipment. He will find many uses for it.

When these magnifiers are mounted on stands that provide a stage, spring clips, mirror, adjustable and focusing arm, and usually hand rests, the outfit is termed a *dissecting microscope*. While designed primarily for biological work, such instruments are valuable in many other fields as well.

COMPOUND MICROSCOPES   We have seen that whether a microscope is simple is determined not by the number of its lenses but by the fact that it forms a single image. A *compound microscope*, while it always contains more than one lens, is defined rather as one that first produces a real image, then remagnifies this as a second, virtual image. It is one microscope upon another, hence compound.

The kind of compound microscope whose parts we have described has, strangely enough, never been given a standard name agreed upon by all manufacturers. With the simplest optical equipment, it is commonly known as a *school microscope;* with standard optics it is a *laboratory microscope;* or either of these may be called a *biological microscope* or a *student microscope*. With the addition of a substage condenser, oil-immersion objective, and a mechanical stage, our instrument becomes a *medical microscope* (Fig. 10), since these parts are specified by medical schools and are needed in blood counts and bacteriology. Our basic instrument is *monocular*, in that it has a single body tube and eyepiece, and in this way

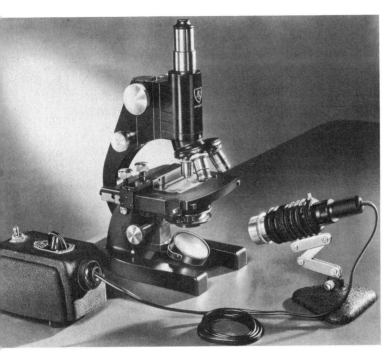

Fig. 10. A modern medical microscope, shown with a universal type of lamp, adjustable to any position. (Courtesy American Optical Co.)

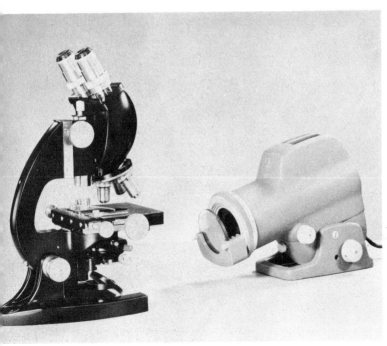

Fig. 11. High-powered binocular microscope with inclined body, shown with research-type lamp. (Courtesy Bausch & Lomb.)

it contrasts with the more expensive *binocular microscope* (Fig. 11), which may have either a vertical or an inclined body and may have interchangeable monocular and binocular bodies, in which case the monocular is used for photomicrography. Research microscopes are of this type. Our biological microscope is also *monobjective*, whereas there are instruments, usually termed *wide-field binoculars*, that are both binocular and *binobjective* (Fig. 12). Wide-field binoculars, while expensive because they are virtually two microscopes side by side, are much preferred in the observation of a host of relatively large objects, such as parasites and embryos; insects and small plant parts, such as flowers and seeds; coins, stamps, textiles, paper, fingerprints, bullet scratches, and documents. Their magnifications are in the low range, approximately from 4× to 20×. It should be stressed that this kind of instrument is not a competitor of the monocular microscope; the two supplement each other. All large laboratories are equipped with both. Latest of titles is 3-D microscope.

Fig. 12. Wide-field binocular microscope. (Courtesy E. Leitz.)

Fig. 13. Testa model F microscope.

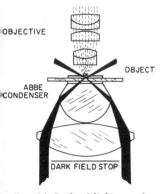

OBJECTIVE

OBJECT

ABBE CONDENSER

DARK FIELD STOP

Fig. 14. Path of light rays in dark-field illumination. (Courtesy Bausch & Lomb.)

Another instrument that has never received a satisfactory and generally accepted title is the so-called *amateur microscope*. Actually, it is an *elementary* or *miniature* model; an amateur microscopist may of course own from the poorest to the finest, or even a whole laboratory full, of standard scientific instruments. Elementary microscopes will prove entirely satisfactory for beginning and survey work, if their objectives are achromatic. There are a number of good American, German, and Japanese instruments of this class available (Fig. 13).

The *comparison microscope* (Fig. 101, Chapter 13) is the reverse of the binocular, since it is a monocular-binobjective type. It permits simultaneous comparison, side by side, of two different specimens, located on two different stages or on two parts of one stage, and is extremely useful in scientific crime detection, as in comparing bullets, fingerprints, stains, etc. *Chemical* and *petrographic* (rock-studying) *microscopes* (Fig. 58, Chapter 9) have circular stages that revolve; they are equipped with apparatus for polarizing the incident light and with various accessories needed in studying by this method. They are used to identify crystals and are needed in mineralogy, an important member of the geological family of sciences. *Shop microscopes* are of several styles, but all are made specially for examining raw materials, manufacturing processes, and finished products in industry; indeed, they control the uniformity and quality of the product. The operator inspects, for instance, the screw thread of a sample bolt, picked from the bin at random; or he wants to know if the weave of a piece of Nylon goods is even, or if the spread of pigment in paint is fine enough, or if an alloy of steel contains the right amount of nickel, properly distributed. *Projection microscopes* (Fig. 31, Chapter 4) throw the real image on a screen, to accompany a lecture or quiz, or downward upon a table, for drawing.

DARK FIELD   In *dark-field optics* a stop is placed below the condenser in such a way that all central light is blocked off (Fig. 14) and only marginal light is allowed to pass. Thus the solid cone of light ordinarily supplied by the condenser is converted to a hollow cone. This marginal light illuminates the object but passes thence out of the optical pathway, not going

Fig. 15. Mosquito antenna, 85×. Left: *bright field;* right: *dark field.*

up the tube. The field, in this method, appears completely black. Fine structures of the object, however, reflect some of the incident light up the tube and seem to the observer to be self-luminous. They glow brilliantly in a black field, so that dark-field optics has proved a useful adjunct method to reveal the surface markings of objects, as well as to demonstrate small, transparent bodies that would otherwise remain invisible. Figure 15 shows the appearance of the same subject under bright field and dark field. Any microscope equipped with a condenser can be used for dark-field studies. The manufacturer supplies the stop for this purpose, to be inserted in the filter carrier. There are also special types of condensers (*paraboloid, cardioid*) for special refinements of this technique.

PHASE CONTRAST   A recent major discovery is the *phase-contrast* principle. By controlling the character of the light waves that make up the image, small differences in contrast can be accentuated so that components of material appearing more or

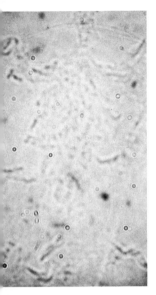

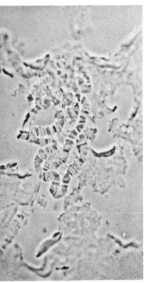

less homogeneous under ordinary microscopes can be made to stand out in striking contrast. Such instruments are used mainly in studying unstained objects, notably living cells, and have wide applications in biology, medicine, and industry. Figure 16 shows the same subject photographed by nonphase and by phase, to demonstrate the advantages of the latter. The cost of special parts has limited this useful technique to the larger laboratories; recently, however, United Scientific Company (Unitron) has marketed a Japanese phase-contrast instrument in the lower price bracket, within the reach of anyone who can afford a standard laboratory nonphase microscope. It can be used for both phase and nonphase work and gives satisfactory results for all ordinary purposes.

REFLECTING MICROSCOPES Thus far we have been discussing the *refracting microscope*. However, a practice that was experimented with in the seventeenth and eighteenth centuries has now been revived—the production of enlarged images by means of mirrors instead of lenses. The instrument that produces an image in this way is a *reflecting microscope*. One great advantage in using a concave mirror to bring incident light rays to a focus is the fact that, since the rays do not enter or pass through the glass, they suffer no dispersion; consequently there is no chromatic aberration and thus no expensive correction for this major defect. Figure 17 shows a recent reflecting objective.

ELECTRON OPTICS The *electron microscope* is a twentieth-century addition to the family of optical instruments. Electron beams can be converged or diverged either by electromagnets or by an electrostatic field, and thus brought to a focus. Their waves have such a very high frequency of vibration, and the consequent wavelengths are so extremely short, that such a beam can disclose much smaller detail than can be seen with a light microscope. An analogy has been made between these two kinds of microscopes and two fish nets, one coarse and one fine in mesh. You cannot catch minnows with a salmon net; nor, if we use visible light as the medium for revealing very small objects, can we see those that are less in diameter than one-half a wavelength of light. With ultraviolet optics, where the wavelengths are shorter, the *resolution* (ability to distinguish fine detail clearly) is greater. With the advent of the new science of electronics, physicists and engineers devised a way to utilize a viewing medium whose wavelengths were far shorter still—the electron beam.

The first electron microscopes were very large. A high voltage and a vacuum tube to discharge the stream of electrons were essential. As the element of danger in such an instrument is obvious, the operator had to be shielded by heavy casings around the transformer and other parts. Glass will not transmit electrons, so the specimens are mounted on collodion films; air will not pass electrons, hence the tube of this microscope is a housing containing a high vacuum, and means had to be invented for passing specimens in and out through an air lock, without breaking the vacuum. The lenses (condenser, objective, projector) in the RCA electromagnetic type of instrument (Fig. 18) are magnets that deflect the stream so as to focus the waves upon the specimen and thence to a fluorescent screen, where the image may be viewed or photographed.

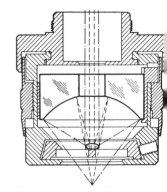

Fig. 17. Beck's reflecting objective.

Fig. 18. RCA Electron Microscope, model EMU-3.

Obviously a mechanism of this kind is not for the uninitiated, entirely aside from the cost. Most universities now possess an electron microscope and offer a course in how to use it. The size and complexity have continually been reduced, so that today's table model (Fig. 18) bears little resemblance to the relatively crude early instruments. Ease of operation has been greatly increased, and the cost lowered, though the price still taxes the budget of the small laboratory. The first results, though sensational, were disappointing to the biologist. A single bacterium could be blown up to the size of a golf ball, but the magnification was empty, i.e., it was *magnification without resolution*. Merely making an object larger without showing greater detail is a useless accomplishment. As many refinements were developed in electron techniques, the resolution has steadily improved, and now these microscopes are revealing structures never before seen. Virus studies have profited greatly. It must be stressed that this instrument is still in its infancy and that we may expect many further advances. Magnifications range from 1,500× to 25,000× and can be further enlarged photographically up to 100,000×. Recent discoveries have upped this figure to the neighborhood of five million. This instrument is not to be regarded as a replacement for or even a competitor of the light microscope, but as a partner—a valuable addition to the family that can contribute further information. The light microscope will doubtless always be the basic tool.

FURTHER HISTORY   Some time before Leeuwenhoek, at the end of the sixteenth century, the first compound microscopes were made. As with simple microscopes, there is controversy as to who should be honored as the inventor, but there are many historians who feel that credit should go to Zacharias Jansen, a lens grinder of Middleburg, Holland. He and his father made and sold spectacles, and it is said that while experimenting with the idea of constructing a telescope, he accidentally aligned certain of his lenses in a sliding tube in such fashion as to present a magnified view of a near object. The date assigned is 1591, and it is known definitely that between that date and 1608 Jansen built both fly glasses (microscopes) and spyglasses (telescopes) with his tubes.

Fig. 19. Robert Hooke's compound microscope, 1665.

Between 1608 and 1610 Galileo, having heard that "a Dutchman" had built both instruments, stated that he could do the same, and he proceeded to do so. Since he was a recognized scientist and made his results known to the scientific world, he became the "effective inventor" of both the microscope and the telescope, though his name has become associated primarily with the latter. Robert Hooke, secretary of the then newly formed Royal Society of London, owned one of the more elaborate and ingenious of early compound microscopes (Fig. 19). From left to right in the illustration there is a reservoir of oil for the illuminating flame (imagine anyone working with such a feeble light source today), a condenser to focus these light rays upon the object, an object holder, or stage, then the microscope proper, with adjustments both horizontally (mechanical stage) and vertically. In 1665 Hooke wrote the beautifully illustrated *Micrographia*,[1] showing for the first time numerous miscellaneous objects as seen with his microscope.

Eighteenth-century models ran from the extreme of complete simplicity seen in a wooden microscope of Nuremberg around 1750 (Fig. 20) to the extreme of the rococo instrument of the same period at the French court (Fig. 21). Early improvements were mainly mechanical. In the nineteenth century the microscope began to take on its modern appearance, as in the Oberhauser, 1846, instrument. No change of basic importance was made in the optical parts until Hall, in England in 1733, made achromatic telescope objectives, and John Dollond, an English optician, also made such parts in 1757 and let his results be known.

One of the first to apply the principles of Hall and Dollond to microscope objectives was C. L. Chevalier, Paris physician, in 1825. His work met with such success that he founded the firm of Chevalier & Son, the first company to manufacture microscopes commercially. In London, Smith and Beck associated as a business, now R. & J. Beck. Andrew Ross, also in London, entered the field in 1832 and made a number of important improvements; and this same year saw the beginning

Fig. 20. *Eighteenth-century wooden microscope of Nuremberg.*

Fig. 21. *Rococo model of microscope of the French Court in the eighteenth century. (Photo by Underwood & Underwood.)*

[1] A modern reprint of this famous work is available: Robert Hooke, *Micrographia*, 1665. A facsimile edition was published by R. T. Gunther in *Early Science in Oxford*, vol. XIII: *The Life and Works of Robert Hooke* (Part V), Oxford University Press, New York, 1938.

of yet another British firm, Powell & Leland. Nachet began in Paris in 1845, and a year later Carl Zeiss started his famous works at Jena, Germany. In 1869 Ernst Leitz took over the shops of Kellner, in Wetzlar, Germany.

In America, the pioneer manufacturer of microscopes was Charles A. Spencer, of Canastota, New York. In 1847 he first made microscopes for commercial sale and thus founded the future Spencer Lens Company, located some while later in Buffalo. In 1935 this company was acquired by the American Optical Company, Southbridge, Massachusetts, becoming the Scientific Instrument Division of this great modern-day company of spectacle makers.

In 1872 Edward Bausch, son of one of the founders of Bausch & Lomb, a business begun in 1853, made his first microscope (Fig. 22) and later was the first to apply modern machine production methods and assembly-line practices to this rapidly growing industry. William Watson & Sons Company of London entered the microscope field in 1875. Joseph Zentmayer in 1877 and J. W. Queen & Company in 1896, both of Philadelphia, became important American competitors.

Toward the end of the century a remarkable combination occurred at Jena. Professor Ernst Abbe, the scientist and mathematician; Carl Zeiss, the manufacturer; Otto Schott, the glassmaker; and the German government, through subsidies, combined to produce the finest objectives yet known, as well as many special inventions and improvements. The Italian, Amici, had perfected immersion objectives, but Abbe now designed supercorrected ones which he termed apochromatics, the substage condenser bearing his name, a camera lucida, refractometer, and many other items of importance. It was generally held that the light microscope had reached its limits.

Today we would not be this rash in making statements. As we have seen, improvements can come from unexpected sources and can be based on hitherto unsuspected principles. Dark field, polarized light, and ultraviolet have augmented the microscopist's methods. Now we have the new phase-contrast principle as a major addition. The pioneer work on this invention was by Frits Zernicke, a professor at Groningen, Holland, in 1935. He induced Zeiss to manufacture phase-contrast equipment. Electron optics may be said to have had its

Fig. 22. First microscope made by Edward Bausch, in 1872.

birth in Germany in 1926–1927 in the calculations of H. Busch, who presented the theory of the electron lens. The first successful instrument was that of the firm of Siemens & Halske, Berlin, in 1938. In the United States, the chief improvements have been developed under the leadership of Vladimir Zworykin, of RCA.

The two major American manufacturers of optical instruments

American Optical Company, Scientific Instrument Division, Buffalo 15, N.Y. (formerly the Spencer Lens Company).
Bausch & Lomb Optical Company, Rochester 2, N.Y.

Other manufacturers and dealers

C. A. Brinkman & Co., 378–380 Great Neck Rd., Great Neck, L.I., N.Y. Dealer in German microscopes and scientific instruments.

Cooke, Troughton & Simms, Inc., 110 Pleasant St., Malden 48, Mass. Cooke microscopes, other optical instruments, parts, optics, accessories. (U.S. corporation of famous British firm.)

Edmund Scientific Corporation, Barrington, N.J. Manufacturer and importer, all sorts of optical equipment.

Ercona Corporation, Scientific Instrument Division, 527 Fifth Ave., New York 17, N.Y. Optical instruments; American agents for Carl Zeiss, Jena.

Gotham Scientific Company, 106 Water St., New York 5, N.Y. Dealer, scientific equipment; importer Tiyoda (Japanese) microscopes.

Graf-Apsco Company, 5868 Broadway, Chicago 40, Ill. Dealer, Kremp (German) microscopes; new and reconditioned microscopes of all makes; repairs and supplies.

William J. Hacker & Company, Inc., 82 Beaver St., New York 5, N.Y. Dealer, scientific instruments; importer, Reichert (Austrian) microscopes.

Halco Scientific Instrument Company, 957 Springdale Rd., N.E., Atlanta 6, Ga. Dealer in German and Austrian microscopes and instruments.

E. Leitz, Inc., 468 Fourth Ave., New York 16, N.Y. The New York office of this major German firm.

Harry Ross, 61 Reade St., New York 7, N.Y. Dealer in new and reconditioned microscopes of all types; instruments, supplies.

Schultz Surgical Instrument Company, 59 Pearl St., New York 4, N.Y. Dealer and importer; Schultz (Japanese) microscopes.

Eric Sobotka, 100 W. 42d St., New York 36, N.Y. Dealer in Swiss, German, and Austrian microscopes and accessories.

Testa Manufacturing Company, 10130 E. Rush St., El Monte, Calif. Makers of Testa microscopes and other optical items.

United Scientific Company, 204–206 Milk St., Boston 9, Mass. Importers, Unitron (Japanese) microscopes; general science dealers.

Carl Zeiss, Inc., 485 Fifth Ave., New York 17, N.Y. The New York office for Zeiss-Winkel microscopes and other instruments.

chapter three

Using the microscope

Operation of a microscope is not difficult, but it is important for any beginner to learn to use this great instrument correctly. Some of the manipulations become automatic habits, difficult to change once formed—all the more reason for establishing good habits from the start. The following instructions are intended for those who will work at home, without the supervision of a classroom teacher, but many of the statements will be applicable to other situations.

Use a substantial table located in a suitable place as your laboratory worktable. If there is a possibility of doing some of the work in the daytime, place the table across a window; otherwise, all of the work may be done by artificial light. One or more electric outlets will be needed, and access to a sink. Some persons prefer a chair, others a stool; it doesn't matter which you use as long as the height is such that you can sit naturally, without craning upward or stooping downward. When you are looking into the microscope, your body should lean slightly forward and your head should be inclined somewhat downward, but the position should be a natural, comfortable one, not strained or cramped.

To transport the microscope from one place to another, carry it by the arm. If it is a large and heavy model, place the left hand under the base, to help in support and to increase safety. The two things to avoid are holding the instrument in an inverted position so that the eyepiece could fall out, and banging the stand against the edge of the table top or a shelf. Remember, this a precision instrument; never treat it roughly. Place it upon the table gently; guide it into its box carefully. If used in this way, a microscope should last a lifetime or longer.

As you sit at the table stand the instrument squarely in front of you and keep it there. Do not shove it aside when the time comes to do other things; move your stool instead, and always guard against knocking the microscope over by sudden and incautious movements of your hands. If it is directly in front of you and close to your body, you are not likely to knock against it. The tube of the microscope faces away from you, the arm toward you, except in a few modern research stands of so-called "reversed microscopes."

Setting up the microscope

Now let us assume that you have never used a microscope and know nothing about proper procedure. If you will follow the suggested steps given here and play the role of a beginner, correct methods will become habits from the start, or bad habits will be changed to desirable ones.

With nothing as yet on the stage of the microscope, and the low-power objective in the optic axis, look down the tube with the left eye and keep the right eye open. Do not squint; let the eyes relax and gaze without strain, as if looking off at a distant view. Grasp the mirror frame with the thumb and forefinger of each hand; this gives the best hold on the mirror for twisting and turning it to set it at the right inclination.

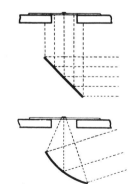

Fig. 23. Use of mirror on a microscope without a condenser. (Courtesy Bausch & Lomb.)

RULES FOR USE OF THE MIRROR *For microscopes without a condenser:* When working with daylight, use the plane mirror. Adjust the mirror frame so as to catch the light from fleecy white clouds as first choice, clear blue sky as second. Never try to focus directly on the sun; it is far too strong as a light source. The rays received are parallel and should be directed straight up the tube by the mirror, as in Figure 23, top. Daylight not only is variable according to time of day and weather conditions, but also not available much of the time when

36

many persons are free to work at their microscope. For these reasons a great many microscopists prefer to use artificial light at all times. As will be explained in detail in the following chapter, illumination from special lamps is essential for all advanced work. If a microscope lamp is used without a condenser, employ the concave mirror, which will collect more rays than will the plane side, and concentrate them on the object, as shown in Figure 23, bottom.

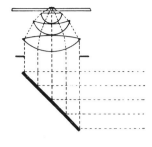

For microscopes equipped with a substage condenser:

Always use the plane mirror. As shown in Figure 24, the condenser is designed to focus incident light from the plane mirror upon the object, whereas if the concave mirror is used these rays will focus below the object, lowering the efficiency of the condenser.

The bright circle of light seen in looking down the tube is the *field* of the microscope. The mirror should be so set that the field is uniformly illuminated, without shadows, crossbars, or other uneven appearances. The *amount* of light should now be regulated by operating the iris or disk diaphragm, observing the effect on the illumination. The proper quantity, in work without a condenser, is moderate—neither so bright as to produce glare, nor so dim as to demand effort on the part of the observer in trying to see something that is improperly illuminated.

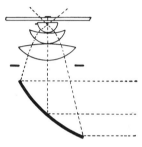

Fig. 24. Use of mirror on a microscope with a condenser. (Courtesy Bausch & Lomb.)

THE SLIDE   Select a finished slide for inspection. A preliminary listing of the steps in microtechnique by which certain slides are prepared will be useful at this time as a preview of what is to come and to give you a healthy respect for the value of slides. A cross section of plant stem or leaf or of an animal organ will serve our purpose; examine such a specimen carefully for a moment; there is much more to it than meets the eye.

The foundation is the *glass slide*, usually termed *glass slip* in England; its standard size is 3 by 1 in., though there are larger and smaller dimensions for special purposes. The glass is an especially fine and clear grade, free from bubbles and scratches, noncorrosive, with both surfaces polished and the edges ground so that fingers will not be cut during handling. Upon the center of the slide is placed the *object*, but before it is ready for mounting it must be put through an extraordinary series of processes that involves detaching the part from its original environment, fixing (preserving) it against decay, washing out excess fixer, removing water (dehydration) and substituting for it a fluid that will mix with paraffin so as to embed the piece of tissue in this wax, which supports soft parts while thin sections are being cut. After sectioning, a single, extremely thin slice is fastened to a blank slide, and the paraffin is removed. Gradually the slide is passed through a series of fluids that end in water (hydration), in which it can be stained with hematoxylin, a dye that colors the nuclei of cells blue; then it must go back through the series so that excess hematoxylin can be washed out and so that the section can be dehydrated and brought into eosin, the counterstain that tints the rest of the cell red, affording contrast. Finally the tissue is made more nearly transparent, by means of an oil, and then brought into balsam or some other mountant. Balsam is a natural resin, fluid when applied but hardening to a solid in time. There are synthetic substitutes that are better than balsam.

The mount is capped with a *cover glass,* of the same fine quality as the slide, but exceedingly thin; then, after drying, the slide is cleaned and labeled. The label should give the name of the object, the view presented, and how the tissue was prepared.

In handling finished slides, hold them by the edges or by the labeled part; a fine fingerprint in oil (the skin is always oily) may be interesting in crime detection but will certainly obscure the view of the object if it is on the cover glass. Never stack slides one on top of another; the pressure frequently melts the mounting medium and causes slides to stick together, often ruining them completely. Never place a spring clip on top of the coverglass of a finished slide; the glass may crack or the pressure may ruin the specimen. Never strew slides about the work table; they are likely to become buried under papers, books, or specimens, and ruined slides will result. When they are not in use, keep them in slide boxes or cabinets.

FOCUSING Place the slide crossways on the stage of the microscope, one spring clip over the label, the other over the blank glass on the right, the specimen over the aperture. Press down on the knobs that secure the spring clips to the stage so that the slide is held firmly in place. With the base of the left hand press down on the left side of the horseshoe base while grasping the arm of the microscope with the right hand. Pull back on the arm until the tube is inclined at an angle suited to your height, for ease and comfort of observation. This is not done if your instrument has an inclined body tube.

Lower the head to the level of the stage, at one side of the tube, so that you may look closely at the clearance between objective and coverglass, then lower the objective until it is within about ¼ in. of the slide. Now, looking down the tube, turn the coarse adjustment head slowly toward you so as to raise the tube. Very shortly the object should come into view; focus it approximately with the coarse adjustment and then accurately with the fine adjustment.

This procedure is known as "focusing up," and if it is always followed you will never crack a valuable slide or damage a still more valuable objective. The careless or improperly coached microscopist may look into the tube and start turning the adjustment so as to run the tube downward; he may easily flash past the focal plane without seeing it and go on down until the objective hits the slide, usually with unfortunate results. On many microscopes there is a stop intended to prevent this contact, but even so if the slide is a thick mount, the accident can happen. It is certainly a simple and wise precaution always to focus up. The proper execution of this procedure is an indication of the well-trained operator.

While observing the object, grasp the slide at each end with the thumb and forefinger of each hand and move it to left or right and then up or down, noting that motions are reversed under the microscope and that a very little movement produces a large apparent one, speed as well as size being magnified. If the object has parts that should be orientated correctly, it will have to be placed on the stage upside down. Take for example, a whole mount of a flea; mount the slide on the stage with the flea lying on his back and he will then appear right side up when viewed through the tube. This reversal of normal space relations and movements of the hands is a bit awkward at first, but adjusting to it soon becomes second nature. Strangely enough, this habit is more difficult to unlearn than to acquire. When wide-field binoculars, which yield an erect image and do not reverse motions, came into use, those who were experienced with monocular instruments found it very difficult to unlearn the reversals to which they were accustomed.

With the low-power objective sharply focused, again lower the head to the side of the tube and, while watching carefully to see that the objective does not hit the slide, slowly change to the high-dry objective. It is correctly aligned when a click is felt, and it should not strike the slide. Look in the tube again to see if the object is in focus, or approximately so. It should need only a slight movement of the fine adjustment to sharpen the focus. If this is the condition, the microscope is said to be *parfocal*. All microscopes are parfocal when they leave the factory, but if you are using an old or secondhand instrument, it may have gotten out of adjustment to such an extent that when the high power is swung into line, nothing shows in the field. If the object is centered over the aperture so that something could be expected to show, then the objective is out of focus. Repeat the preceding operation: lower the head to the side, lower the objective until it barely clears the coverglass, look down the tube and focus up, very slowly. It is easy to flash past this focal point and miss it.

If the objectives are not parfocal, the condition may be quite annoying and should be corrected. Determine, by trying first the low and then the high power, which one focuses nearest the object. The other, in such a case, will have to be *lowered* to come into focus. Unscrew this objective from the nosepiece and cut a shim to fit around the base of the screw threads. A shim is a very thin collar of narrow rim that will fit over the threads and prevent the objective from screwing down as far as it would without the shim. It can be cut from tissue paper, linen paper, or very thin metal foil, according to the thickness required to lower the objective to the proper level where, when screwed back onto the nosepiece, it will be more or less parfocal with the other objective. A bit of trial and error here will enable you to secure an approximate parfocality, suitable for most purposes.

Observe that the illumination of the field is dimmer with

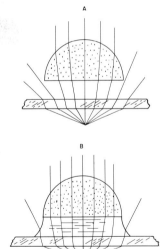

Fig. 25. A: *High-dry objective; marginal rays refracted away and lost.* B: *oil-immersion; marginal rays refracted through lens and saved.*

the high power. The reason for this lies in the smaller aperture of the front lens of the high-power objective, which admits a smaller cone of light than does the low-power front lens, and also in the fact that the number of separate components and elements is considerably greater in the high-power objective. A certain amount of the incident light is lost by absorption and reflection at each surface of each lens.

If your microscope has *coated optics*, much of this loss is prevented. A hard-surface, low-reflection coating is applied during the manufacturing process, resulting in clearer, crisper images. Various companies have their trade names for such coatings: "Americote" is the term used by American Optical, "Balcote" by Bausch & Lomb.

The procedure for using the oil-immersion objective is somewhat different. The light must be quite a bit stronger to begin with, and the details of illumination (explained in the next chapter) are much more important with this objective. The slide is set up and focused with the low-power objective, called a "finder" objective when used to locate objects that are to be studied under high magnification. Center the object carefully, so that when the 97× objective is swung into line, the object will appear in the field. Use the high-dry objective, if you wish, as a checkup. Rack the condenser down to secure clearance, and place a drop of immersion oil on the top lens of the condenser, then rack it up and observe that the oil makes contact with the bottom of the slide, spreading out into a film. This act is termed "oiling the condenser to the slide." Next, raise the tube to a considerable clearance, and swing the oil-immersion objective into line. Place a drop of the oil on top of the cover glass, over the center of the aperture, then, looking to the side, lower the tube until the front lens makes contact with the oil. Look into the tube and focus up, very carefully and slowly, until a sharp focus is secured. Adjust the light as may be necessary. Use of oil as a suspension between lens and cover glass in this manner gathers more light— makes a wider cone of incident light (Fig. 25)—and greatly increases resolution.

Comparing the different objectives present on your microscope, it is evident that the higher the magnification the smaller the area of the object seen; it is also evident that the restricted view shows greater detail. The rule is to use the *lowest* power that will show what one wishes to see. The uninitiated are often obsessed with the notion of power and want always to see things at the utmost magnification, but you will probably do more work with the low powers than with the high. With the usual compound microscope there is more often a need for lower rather than for higher powers; remember, you can get so close that you can't see the woods for the trees. If the woods are the object of your quest, then you need low powers; if the trees, you need higher magnification; if the bark of one tree, then you need the highest of all.

ANGULAR AND NUMERICAL APERTURES   Every objective has a definite limit to the width of the cone of light it can pick up from the object; this, not the magnifying power, limits the fineness of detail that it can render distinguishable. This capacity is the *resolution*, or *resolving power*, of the objective, its most important property. The width of the widest possible cone of light is its *angular aperture*. As long as all objectives were made to be used dry, with air between front lens and cover glass, their angular apertures could be compared and could serve as an index to their resolving powers, but when various inventors made first water-immersion, then glycerin-immersion, and finally oil-immersion objectives, a new means of comparison was needed. Abbe introduced the concept of *numerical aperture* (N.A.), equal to $n \sin u$, where n is the refractive index of the medium between front lens and cover glass, and u is one-half the angular aperture of the objective. By taking half the angle in every case, the cones are converted to right angles; this makes it possible to compare their sines, which is to say the ratios of two sides, as a trigonometric function. Another way of stating this is to say that u is the angle between the extreme marginal ray of light and the axial ray entering the objective. The *refractive index* of a substance is the ratio, expressed in sines, between the angle of incidence and the angle of refraction of light rays transmitted by that substance.

Reexamine the objectives on your microscope. Engraved on each casing are a number of items whose meaning you should know. There will be the name and address of the maker and in many cases a serial number. This number is of great assistance in identifying lost or stolen objectives; it also enables the manufacturer to determine when the part was made and according to what formula, should repairs or cleaning ever become necessary. Then there is the *equivalent focus*, the focal distance of all the elements and components of the objective acting together, stated in terms of the focal distance of a single ideal lens, equivalent in this respect to the whole objective. This is usually 16-mm. for the low-dry. 4-mm. for the high-dry, and 1.8-mm. for the oil-immersion objectives. On modern objectives the magnifying power is generally stated, as for example, 10×. Lastly there is a figure, either with or without the prefix N.A., which designates numerical aperture and which is hence a measure of the resolution of the objective. Frequently seen as N.A.'s on today's objectives are 10× —0.25; 43×—0.65; 97×—1.25.

All dry objectives have N.A.'s of less than 1; oil-immersion objectives have N.A.'s greater than 1. Since N.A. is a mathematical rating based on the width of the cone of light an objective can utilize, the higher figures mean better performance. However, 0.25, though it seems very small by comparison with 1.25, is ample for the low-dry objective. The focal distance of this objective necessitates a tall narrow cone of light; only those objectives focusing very close to the object can receive a short wide cone.

There must be a relationship between the magnification and the N.A. of any objective. If the magnification is too low, fine detail is not rendered sufficiently visible. Equally, with adequate magnification, if the N.A. is too low, the detail will remain unresolved. Both must be proper for the purpose at hand. If the magnification is greater than required by a given N.A., then no further detail is seen but only larger images that yield no additional information. This is *empty magnification*. The rule generally used is to employ no higher magnification than 1,000 times the N.A. of any objective; this is the upper limit, applying to persons with perfect eyesight. For many, 700 to 800 would be a more realistic factor. Another rule is to match the N.A. of condenser and objective. For example, the 1.40 objective is more expensive than the 1.25. If used, it must be combined with a condenser of N.A. 1.40 in order for it to achieve its full effectiveness; if used with a condenser rated at 1.25, the N.A. of the system is immediately reduced to 1.25, just as failure to oil the condenser to the slide reduces the N.A. to 1. A chain is no stronger than its weakest link.

Cleaning the microscope

The mechanical parts can be kept free from dust by using a soft cloth, supplemented by a soft brush to reach parts, such as the teeth in the rack-and-pinion gear, that are inaccessible to the cloth. A camel's-hair brush or small, inexpensive water-color brush is suggested. Do not use any oil; the finely made parts do not need lubrication, and oil will only gum and clog and collect dust. The great enemy of the microscope is *dust*. It is important to keep the instrument covered at all times when not in use. Store it in its case, or use a plastic hood. Many microscopes are provided with both when purchased; if not, either item may be bought separately.

To detect which of the optical parts may be the guilty party when the image shows foreign matter, streaks, or fog, go through the following routine: With the microscope set up and focused on a slide, press the ball of the thumb lightly on the eye lens of the eyepiece. Look down the tube and at the same time rotate the eyepiece slowly in its housing by twirling the flange of its upper edge. Anything soiling the eye lens—the oily streaks of a thumbprint in this case—will rotate with the eyepiece and cannot be situated elsewhere. Clean the eye lens. Sprinkle a little cigarette ash or talcum powder on the slide and inspect the object through the tube. Move the slide back and forth. Any foreign matter that moves will, of course, lie on the slide. Clean the slide. Make a fingerprint on the front lens of the objective. Now, looking at the object, twirl the eyepiece and move the slide; the obstructing material does not move in either case, proving that it lies on the objective. These two motions, quickly made, locate at once the part where offending matter is lodged. Clean the objective lens. If your microscope has a condenser, rack it up and down, noting that you can focus the image of remote things, such as window bars, clouds, lamp filaments, upon the object. This sort of deformation of the image should not be confused with foreign matter on the microscope or slide.

To clean the optical parts, nothing is better than an old, soft linen handkerchief. A special cleansing paper termed *lens paper* is sold in either sheets or books. Breathe on the part to be cleaned and wipe it immediately, using the moisture from the breath before it evaporates. Repeat several times if necessary. If this does not suffice, use soap and water, sparingly, taking care not to wet more than the surface being cleaned; rinse and wipe dry. If this does not work, alcohol or ether, solvents of greases, may be tried, and finally a very small drop of xylene, the balsam solvent, followed by alcohol. Should the xylene penetrate to the interior of an objective, it might dissolve the balsam used to cement doublets and thus necessitate factory repairs; hence use this solvent with care.

Slides have an annoying habit of becoming dirty or cloudy from no apparent cause; they are always in need of cleaning. The microscope mirror gets dust on it no matter how carefully one stores his instrument. The eye lens nearly always has fine oily stripes caused by the eyelashes. Hence it is excellent laboratory technique, at the beginning of each session of work with the microscope, to clean the mirror, the eye lens, and the bottom of all objectives, as a matter of routine, and then to clean each slide before using it.

In obstinate cases, unscrew both ends of the ocular, remove the separable half of the 10× objective, and clean all exposed surfaces. This should not have to be done often. Never try to take the high-powered objectives apart; sometimes in the tropics a fungus growth occurs inside these parts, and this requires factory attention. Never use anything in connection with the optical parts that could contain any form of grit; optical glass scratches easily; scratches ruin lenses. For this reason, to clean the glass surfaces on your microscope, never use a cloth that has been used to clean the mechanical parts; reserve a special cloth for the lenses, or use lens paper.

Care of the eyes

Rule 1. The most important of all rules for the beginning microscopist is to *keep both eyes open!* This ability is the surest sign of the properly trained and experienced operator; you will never see him squint and close the free eye. He looks into the microscope as if there were no instrument there at all. This is another of those bits of training that soon become habit. Man is an animal with binocular vision; he forms a single, fusion image in the brain of what is seen separately by each eye. Perform this instructive experiment, known as Rogers' illusion: roll a sheet of paper into a tube and look through it with the left eye toward a light or some distinctive object; hold the palm of the right hand in front of the right eye, near the far end of the tube, so as to block off the view of the object from the right eye. The left eye sees the object, the right eye the palm, and the fusion picture in the mind is that of the object seen through a round hole in the palm of the right hand!

Now a further interesting remark about this illusion is that the experienced microscopist may have some difficulty in seeing it, for he has so trained his eyes that, when gazing down a tube, only the image from the eye in use will register. He doesn't see the palm with the right eye at all; the eye not in use reports its messages to the brain, as usual, but they don't register in consciousness. For all the effect it has, for the time being, this eye might as well be blind. This ability is simply a mental trick that is readily acquired with practice. It may not come easily the first day or the second, but stick with it and soon it will be taken for granted.

Rule 2. Use the two eyes alternately for looking into the microscope. Use the right eye one hour and the left the next. This ensures training both eyes and avoids unequal strain on either.

Rule 3. Alternate looking through the microscope with other duties, such as preparation of materials, reading, or other activities. This rule actually takes care of itself, since this routine is the one that the operator will follow in the regular course of his work.

Rule 4. Avoid too bright or too dim a light. Either is bad for the eyes and also for proper observation of the image, defeating the purpose of microscopic study.

Rule 5. Put yourself in the frame of mind of a spectator at a show. When you are at the movies there is nothing that you personally can do to improve the image on the screen. So with the microscope. If you have attended to all the mechanical adjustments properly, providing the right light and exact focus, there is nothing further you can do about the image; so relax, let the microscope do the work, and gaze down the tube as if you were looking down a deep well, with the accommodation of your eyes set at a great distance. In effect this is true; compared with the size of what you are looking at, you are a long distance away. So keep both eyes open, keep the accommodation relaxed, and don't squint or strain or try to see something that the magnification, the resolution, and the illumination do not reveal.

IF YOU WEAR GLASSES   Those who wear spectacles should, as a rule, remove them when looking down the tube of a microscope. The focus and illumination of the instrument can be so adjusted as to compensate for the usual visual defects; moreover the metal rim of the microscope eyepiece will in time scratch and chip the spectacle lens. If glasses must be worn, there are two things the wearer can do about it. First, he can secure from the manufacturer an ocular with a high eyepoint, made especially for this need, and secondly he can buy from any optician a rubber guard for the ocular rim that will prevent damage to spectacle lenses. Or he may prefer to make his own guard by cutting off the tip of a rubber finger cot and pulling this down over the eyepiece, exposing only the eye-lens.

The *eyepoint* of a microscope is that location just above the eye lens (Fig. 4) where the principal rays of emerging light cross. If the eye is placed at this point, the pupil of the eye will be filled with light from the microscope to the fullest capacity, and the picture thrown on the retina—actually a projected real image—will contain the maximum number of image-forming rays.

Locating objects in the field

Frequently you will wish to show someone else a particular specimen, surrounded by many other objects, and this you can do in any of several ways.

If there are not too many similar objects close together, a verbal description may be sufficient, and in such a case the field is mentally divided into sectors corresponding to the numerals on the face of a clock. One says, for example, "Is that an artery or a vein at two o'clock?" or "Look at that section of a hair about halfway from the center to 7:30."

Often there is need for greater precision, and then a *pointer* should be placed in the eyepiece, as noted on page 12. Take an inch-long portion of a straight hair and stretch it across the middle of the upper surface of the eyepiece diaphragm, embedding each end in a tiny spot of balsam, Duco, or other cement. Allow to harden, then snip the hair in two just to one side of the center with scissors and remove the longer half together with its fleck of adhesive. Reassemble the eyepiece, and the pointer is ready for use. By both rotating the eyepiece and moving the slide, the end of the pointer may be placed upon any object desired.

The demonstration eyepiece is an accessory that enables a teacher to instruct or quiz a student by means of a movable pointer, each person gazing simultaneously into one of the two oculars. It is particularly indicated in studying living material that moves about, and is inserted in the tube of any standard microscope in place of the regular ocular. It would therefore be a desirable adjunct whenever two people are to study together.

Locating objects on the slide

In certain kinds of work, such as that with chromosomes, bacteria, or blood cells, it not infrequently happens that the operator discovers just the stage or type he wants and, after a session of work, wishes to mark this particular object for future reference. Here again there is a choice of method. It will often suffice to raise the objective high above the slide and make a small circle in ink in the center of the field; the 48-mm. objective or other available optical aid may help here. Refocus to see if the wanted object is within the circle of ink; if not, repeat. If so, let the ink dry, reverse the slide, and trace this circle again in ink on the reverse side. When dry, remove the first circle with a moistened cloth. Now you have an indicator circle on the back of the slide, within whose confines the object should lie, permitting fairly rapid location.

If the microscope is equipped with a mechanical stage, coordinates may be read on the measuring scales and a card-index record made of the slide, objective in use, and the readings. Later, if the same setup is duplicated, the same cell or other object should appear in the center of the field. Also available is the Sulzner Location Finder, similar but simpler; that is, it is clamped on the right edge of the stage and permits coordinate readings. There are *locator slides* on the market, consisting of rows and columns of numerals, reduced photographically. The operator has found, let us say, a perfect stage of cell division he wishes to mark for future reference, possibly for photographing. He centers this cell under his high-dry objective, removes the slide, and mounts the locator slide in its place, without disturbing the mechanical stage. Suppose No. 257 is now in the center of the field. In the future, he has only to reverse this procedure. Referring to his card record, he sets up the same microscope with the same objective and gets 257 on the locator slide in the exact center of the field; he then replaces this slide with the one containing the desired cell. One advantage of the locator slide is that it may be used without a mechanical stage if the operator provides a vertical and a horizontal base line against which to align all slides used. Temporary lines may be established with a pencil or Scotch Tape; more permanent ones scratched into the stage with a small knife or needle, the incised lines then filled with a white filling compound, and the excess removed.

References to works dealing with the microscope and its use

Allen, R. M., *The Microscope,* D. Van Nostrand Company, Inc., Princeton, N.J., 1940. Excellent work for the general reader; bibliography.

Beck, C., *The Microscope; Theory and Practice,* D. Van Nostrand Company, Inc., Princeton, N.J., 1938. A brief British book dealing with optical theory. For intermediate and advanced students.

Belling, J., *The Use of the Microscope,* McGraw-Hill Book Company, Inc., New York, 1930. Advanced exercises in critical microscopy.

Carpenter, W. B., rev. by W. H. Dallinger, *The Microscope and Its Revelations,* P. Blakiston's Son & Company, Philadelphia, 1901. Out of print. One of the most famous older works; large, many illustrations. A fine addition to your library if you can pick up a used copy.

Clay, R. S., and T. H. Court, *History of the Microscope,* Charles Griffin & Co., Ltd., London, 1932.

Corrington, J. D., *Adventures with the Microscope,* Bausch & Lomb Optical Co., Rochester, N.Y., 1934. Out of print. Introduction to materials and methods of the several sciences that employ the microscope.

Gage, S. H., *The Microscope,* 17th ed., Comstock Publishing Associates, Inc., Ithaca, N.Y., 1941. Best known and most important American work on the subject.

Hall, C. A., *How to Use the Microscope,* 4th ed., Walter J. Black Inc., New York; The Macmillan Co. of Canada, Ltd. Toronto, 1955. A British work on methods.

Lonert, A. C., *Turtox Microscopy Booklet,* General Biological Supply House, Chicago, 1946. Excellent brief pamphlet, fully illustrated.

Marshall, C. R., and H. D. Griffith, *An Introduction to the Theory and Use of the Microscope,* London, 1928. Brief British manual, well illustrated.

Muñoz, F. J., and H. A. Charipper, *The Microscope and Its Use,* Chemical Publishing Co., Inc., New York, 1943. Kinds of microscopes and accessories and how they are employed.

Olliver, C. W., *Intelligent Use of the Microscope,* 2d ed., Chapman & Hall, Ltd., London, 1952. Practical directions; a successful British manual.

Spitta, E. J., *Microscopy,* 3d ed., London, 1920. A large, advanced work for mature microscopists.

chapter four

The accessories of microscopy

One might think that when a microscope is paid for, that is the end of the expense. As a matter of fact, it is only the beginning! This is not meant to discourage the newcomer. He can add to his materials slowly, a few at a time, and can make a great many of the accessories himself. But the truth is that the microscope is a helpless sort of leading man, taken alone, and needs a whole supporting cast of other instruments and apparatus and supplies. Obtaining and maintaining these pieces constitutes a large part of the fun of microscopy.

There are the slides and cover glasses, the processing glassware and chemicals, instruments and specimens from which to make finished preparations for study. These are the materials of microtechnique and will be discussed in the chapters that follow. Properly listed here are such parts as a microscope lamp, which is a must, and such optionals as a mechanical stage, a binocular body, additional eyepieces and objectives, apparatus for drawing or measuring or photography, and equipment for obtaining dark-field illumination or polarized light. These extras are to be added if, as, and when the need and inclination arise. We shall refer to some of them in later chapters.

FOR GENERAL, ELEMENTARY, OR LOW-POWER WORK   Second in importance only to the microscope itself is the source of illumination. A student gooseneck light or other table lamp may be used, but since a special lamp may be purchased at modest cost or made out of simple materials, it is wise to own a *microscope lamp* from the outset.

Commercial models may be procured for as little as $5 or as much as $1,000; hence it would appear that this matter of illumination is of great importance and that there is a type of lamp available for every purpose and every purse. The *substage lamp* (Fig. 1) is adequate for many needs and may be placed directly in front of the mirror of the microscope, or the mirror may be removed and the lamp put on its back beneath the stage aperture.

Homemade lamps are easily constructed and may follow any of several designs. The *coffee-can lamp* (Fig. 26) is made as follows: discard the lid and in the center of the bottom cut out a circular hole in which an electric socket will fit snugly. Punch half a dozen small, equally spaced holes through the side of the can near the bottom, for ventilation; then cut out a semicircle in the side at the top, providing a window through which the light is to emerge. Paint the exterior if desired, but leave the interior bright. Wire and insert the socket, add a 25- to 40-watt frosted bulb, and turn the can bottom end up for use.

Fig. 26. Coffee-can microscope lamp.

The *baking-powder-can lamp* (Fig. 27) is also easy to make. Attach the socket as in the coffee-can lamp. The support is a short length of brass curtain rod, driven into a wooden base. The latter may be round or square, painted or stained, as desired. Hammer and file the upper end of the brass rod until it is flat, and drill it to receive a small bolt. Cut a strip of tin from a second can and wrap this around the waist of the electric socket, above the threads, leaving two tab ends of ½ in. each, which are then drilled to take the bolt. This sleeve now permits the attachment of the lamp to stand; it also permits adjustment at any desired angle, using a thumbscrew as a nut. Paint the exterior of the can, if you wish. The lid should be retained to serve as a cover which will exclude dust when the lamp is not in use. Further, by cutting out a central opening, about

Fig. 27. Baking-powder-can lamp.

one-half the diameter of the lid, but leaving several tab ends to be bent in as holders, you can convert the lid into a filter or condenser holder. By saving a number of lids from the same make of can, you may fasten a different material to each and then secure different effects by changing lids. Old flashlight lenses make fairly good bull's-eye condensing lenses, though better ones may be bought from an optician for a small amount. Many microscopists use a chemical flask filled with water colored a fairly deep blue by the addition of copper sulfate crystals; this stands between lamp and microscope, where it serves as both condenser and filter.

Suitable for both school and home use is the *chalet lamp,* shaped like a miniature house. It can be equipped with from one to four windows, one to a side; and thus a number of people, seated around the four sides of a table, can obtain their illumination from a single bulb. For demonstrations, entertainment, and games with the microscope there is nothing like a turntable; for this purpose either the Scrabble board table or that antique article known as a Lazy Susan, now popular again, will serve. As the turntable is rotated from person to person around the circle, the relative positions of the lamp at the center and microscope at the edge remain the same; the operator selects a slide, focuses, and turns the Susan so that the microscope comes under the eye of the person to his right, and so on around, meanwhile explaining what the guests are to see.

One of the more recent American Optical student microscopes has a slightly elevated base that contains the lamp, permanently aligned. You can make the same arrangement by constructing an *optical bench,* which is a common base on which are mounted any two or more parts of an optical system so that they have a common optic axis. In the present instance, this means a permanent alignment of lamp and microscope so that, once adjusted, the relationship continues. Secure a piece of hardwood of a size suited to your two instruments. Cut a piece of plywood of the same dimensions as the board, place the microscope near one end, centered, trace around the base, and cut out this tracing on a jigsaw. Tack or glue the plywood to the hardwood. Stand the microscope in its base pattern and secure the toes by straps of leather or tape. Mount the lamp at the other end of the bench, either by cutting out the plywood or by means of cleats or angle irons. The microscope may be removed at any time for use elsewhere, but as long as it is on the optical bench, its relation to the lamp is constant. The finished board, painted black, may be carried about as desired and plugged in at any convenient outlet. Needless to say, the original determination of the axis must be made with care.

It is next essential to indicate how these lamps are to be used. With microscopes that have no condenser, the only factors to attend to are proper brilliance and uniformity of illumination. If the lamp is placed squarely in front of the microscope and the plane mirror set plumb and at the correct angle to direct light rays up the tube (Fig. 23), there should be no difficulty about uniformity. Intensity of the light may be controlled by moving the lamp up to or away from the microscope, by employing a filter on either the microscope or the lamp, and by the microscope diaphragm, iris or disk.

A ground-glass or frosted disk for diffused white light, or a blue disk to approximate the values of daylight, may be supplied with the microscope, for insertion in a swing-out holder on the bottom of the stage, directly under the diaphragm. The Corning Glass Company makes a thick, blue Daylite Glass that gives the values for light from the sun; it is widely used in stores for matching colors and can be obtained in circles or rectangles prepared for use with microscope or lamp. Additional diffusing screens are readily made of cellophane, of any preferred colors, and are termed light *filters;* they are used primarily for photomicrography. To make a filter, enclose a square of colored cellophane or gelatin between two lantern slide blanks, 3¼ x 4 in., and bind the edges. Blue, orange, and green filters will be found useful.

FOR ADVANCED HIGH-POWER WORK AND PHOTOMICROGRAPHY Thus far the conditions governing illumination have not been intricate enough to merit separate study; it is when the microscope is equipped with a substage condenser that correct illumination and a knowledge of how to secure it become of the greatest importance. A condenser is itself a microscope and hence must be capable of being focused; usually a rack-and-pinion gear is provided. The purpose of the condenser is to receive parallel rays of light from the lamp and converge them strongly, focusing a wide-angled cone of light upon the specimen and thence into the objective (Fig. 24).

Most condensers permit removal of the top element for work with low-power objectives; this is necessary since the complete condenser has a very short focal length and forms a small image of the light source that will not, as a rule, illuminate the whole low-power field. When the upper element is removed, the remaining condenser has a much longer focal distance and, when racked down, will fill the entire field with light. Also this separable construction makes possible substitution of a dark-field element, necessary in dark-field work.

With the full condenser in place and using either the high-dry or oil-immersion objectives, there are three forms of illumination that can be employed; each of them should be thoroughly mastered by every serious worker with the microscope.

1. Subcritical Illumination. In the nineteenth century there were famous microscopists who made many great discoveries. After 1825 they had achromatic objectives, but we are likely to forget that during most of this era they had no electrical sources for illumination, but employed oil lamps. In spite of this handicap they did marvelous work; one reason was their discovery of the proper way of illuminating the object under the microscope. They operated the condenser and lamp so as to project the image of the lamp flame directly upon the specimen and thus achieved a degree of resolution of detail far superior to that obtained in any other manner. This was called critical illumination.

Today, if we do the same, we meet with the annoyance, in most cases, of seeing an electric lamp filament lying among the parts of the object. In routine work, it will be sufficient to approximate critical illumination, and we may term this *subcritical.* Instead of focusing the condenser so that the image of the light source is thrown upon the specimen, we can interpose a filter disk—of ground glass, Daylite Glass, or some other material—which now becomes our light source. The condenser should almost touch the bottom of the slide. Operate it to see if any grain, flaw, or temporary ink mark on the filter disk can be seen in the specimen. If so, the condenser will have to be racked just a trifle either way until this interference disappears. Now remove the eyepiece and look down the tube, while operating the condenser iris. You can see the iris, opening and closing. Set it so that its aperture coincides with that of the full width of the back lens of the objective, seen down the tube; in other words, see that this back lens is filled with light to its capacity, but do not open the iris beyond this point. On many instruments the condenser iris will have a scale with numbers; set it at the same N.A. as that shown on the objective. This should achieve the same result, i.e., it should fill the back lens with light. This method of illuminating the object will be found much superior to a mere haphazard setup.

If the object is now too brilliant, do not close the iris, but interpose commercial neutral filters, which may be obtained in various densities, between lamp and microscope. Sometimes the material is seen to best advantage, for special purposes, if contrast is increased. Then we can dispense with proper resolution and purposely deform the image, by racking the condenser downward, or by closing the iris, or by both steps. Neither of these steps should ever be taken where the observation of correct fine detail is the aim.

2. Critical Illumination. Here the image of the light source is focused in the plane of the specimen (Fig. 28). This requires special lamps so as to avoid seeing coiled filaments, and proper equipment is somewhat costly. The results justify the expense, however, when one can afford it, as the image is far superior to that obtained by subcritical or simpler methods. There must be no filters or diffusion disks. As in method 1, the back lens of the objective must be completely filled with light, but with the iris cutting off any further marginal rays. This method is used for critical research, whence the name, and may be used for photomicrography, but it will improve any high-power observations.

3. Köhler Illumination. This is now the preferred method for photomicrography and in most cases for visual work as well (Fig. 28). In this system the image of the lamp diaphragm is focused on the specimen. To make this possible, place the lamp about 10 in. in front of the microscope, adjust the mirror, plane surface in use, and secure a focus on the object with the high-dry objective. Now close the iris of the con-

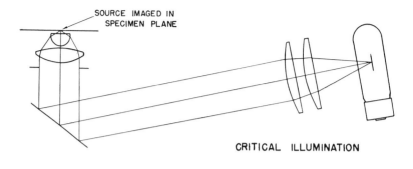

SOURCE IMAGED IN
SPECIMEN PLANE

CRITICAL ILLUMINATION

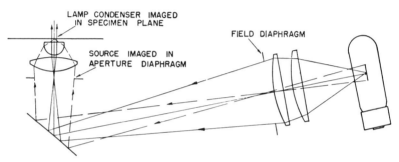

LAMP CONDENSER IMAGED
IN SPECIMEN PLANE

SOURCE IMAGED IN
APERTURE DIAPHRAGM

FIELD DIAPHRAGM

Fig. 28. Critical system (top) and Köhler system (bottom) of illumination compared. (Courtesy Bausch & Lomb.)

denser and look at it from the front by placing your head near the lamp and looking back at the mirror to see the reflection of the iris, strongly illuminated. Rack the lamp condenser back and forth until the filaments of the bulb are focused on the condenser iris, then open this iris to the same N.A. as that of the objective. If there is no scale on the condenser iris, proceed as previously directed: remove the eyepiece, look down the tube, close the iris until it is of the same aperture as the back lens of the objective. Now close the iris diaphragm of the lamp and check to see whether or not its image appears to be lying on the specimen; if not, operate the rack of the microscope condenser until it does. Finally, open the lamp iris to the same N.A. as that of the objective. This method provides Köhler illumination, which will reveal much finer detail than any uncritical arrangement. Use neutral filters to control intensity.

Requirements for lamps used in this class of work include

a rack-and-pinion gear for focusing the lamp condenser, an iris diaphragm, condenser, and filter holder. Some lamps are provided with a water cell for cooling the beam of light, which is occasionally necessary with delicate or living specimens. The *spherical illuminator* is an excellent all-purpose lamp; it may be secured with 100- or 200-watt bulbs or with a 6-volt ribbon-filament lamp to operate with a transformer. The ribbon-filament lamp is much preferred for critical and Köhler illumination, as it provides a plane of light having a uniform intensity all over, and does not obscure parts of the image, as does a coil-filament lamp. The *research illuminator* (Figs. 11, 58) is especially designed to yield critical or Köhler lighting and has all desired features in compact form. For photography or projection there are clock-feed arc lamps, and as the last word in perfection among professional microscope lamps there is the zircon arc, a very costly item.

Built-in units include everything from the lamp alone, to the addition of lamp to condenser, and finally to a most elaborate outfit termed a universal microscope. Frequently seen in laboratories is the attachable form of lamp that plugs in beneath the condenser (Fig. 1). Among the advantages of this style is the permanent alignment of microscope and illuminant; as the microscope is tilted the lamp goes with it. Perhaps the acme in adjustability is seen in lamps like that shown in Figure 10, as this light can be placed in any conceivable position in relation to any form of microscope. The *universal microscope* (Fig. 31), especially favored by Zeiss and Leitz, includes built-in means of obtaining *transmitted light* (coming from below, through the specimen, as in all those instruments we have been discussing thus far), *incident light* (coming from above the stage; reflected light, for the illumination of opaque specimens), dark-field and polarized light, as well as a camera.

Other accessories

In addition to lamps, accessories usually include extra oculars and objectives, condensers, binocular bodies, inclined eyepieces, demonstration eyepieces, and various nosepieces. In addition there should be mentioned here the *comparison eyepiece* (Fig. 101), by means of which any two similar monocular instruments may be converted for the time into a comparison microscope (Chapter 13). *Mechanical stages* may be built in or attachable. The latter type can be bought separately and placed on the microscope as desired. Mechanical stages are essential in any work involving enumeration, as in blood counts.

Hemacytometers (blood cell counters) are included under accessories, though actually they are entirely separate items. The outfit comes in a case and includes a capillary tube with rubber mouthpiece, through which a minute quantity of blood is aspirated and then let out upon a ruled slide, after proper dilution. There are numerous styles of slide rulings, but the purpose of each is to make it possible to count the number of red cells and white cells in a given quantity of blood and then, by multiplication, to arrive at the figure per cubic millimeter. As is well known, the proportions of the red and the various kinds of white cells are of decided importance in diagnosis.

Accessories for use with *polarized light* are numerous. The polarizing microscope (Fig. 58, Chapter 9) is equipped with all necessary parts, but the essentials may be purchased separately for use with other instruments. The two basic parts are the polarizer and analyzer. For ordinary purposes these may consist of sheets of Polaroid film mounted in rings so as to fit the microscope. The film may be bought separately from the Polaroid Corporation for experimental purposes or homemade parts. The *polarizer* slips into the filter ring below the condenser and separates light from the mirror into two rays—the ordinary ray, which is reflected out of the axis, and the extraordinary ray, which continues through but is *polarized*. Unpolarized light vibrates in all directions perpendicular to the direction of travel; polarized light vibrates in only one direction (Fig. 29). The eye cannot detect any difference between polarized and unpolarized light, but when the polarized ray is forced to pass through a second polarizing element, the *analyzer,* situated as a cap on top of the eyepiece, it becomes the ordinary ray for the analyzer; it will or will not be reflected out of the axis, depending on the way the analyzer is manipulated. If the vibration directions of the two Polaroid sheets are set at right angles to each other, no light at all gets through; the polarized ray is extinguished by the analyzer, and the field

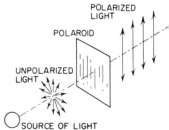

Fig. 29. Plane polarization of light. (Courtesy Polaroid Corporation.)

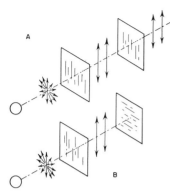

appears black. If, however, the vibration directions are parallel, the ray comes through so as to appear to the eye as ordinary light. Another way of explaining polarization is to say that the "optical slots" of the Polaroids are parallel in the first case (Fig. 30A), crossed in the second (Fig. 30B).

When the slots are crossed, if there is something in the object that will rotate the polarized ray a bit, then when that ray arrives at the analyzer it will not be vibrating at a right angle to that element but at some other angle, and it will be observed, i.e., the object will not be black. Substances that can do this are termed *optically active;* they include a host of materials, such as horn. The geologist and chemist use polarized light to identify crystalline materials (Fig. 64), to learn to what crystal system an unknown substance may belong, and to ascertain other facts about matter. Optically active substances repolarize the extraordinary ray, and during this process some wavelengths are retarded by one-half a wavelength, interfere with one another, and cancel out. Thus some of the wavelengths of white light are missing when the object is seen through such a microscope, and the ones that get through therefore appear colored. Many optically active substances exhibit gorgeous hues under polarization. There have been motion pictures in color showing crystallization of organic chemicals via polarized light—no artist could paint a more brilliantly varied scene.

There are accessories for making measurements under the microscope, for making drawings, and for photography. Measurement under magnification is *micrometry*. In its crudest form no instruments are necessary; measurement is effected by comparisons, an unknown being valued against a known. For example, in sections of human tissues there are almost always some red blood corpuscles in the field; since those of man are known to average very closely around 7.5 microns in diameter, they may be used to compute, by visual comparison, the diameters of such other structures as blood vessels, muscle fibers, or nerve fibers. A micron, the unit of measurement in microscopy, is one-thousandth of a millimeter (0.001 mm.).

Any serious or accurate form of measurement, however, requires the use of micrometers, obtainable from all major optical companies and supply houses. The *stage micrometer* is a thick glass slide upon which a very fine scale has been ruled; it is used as the object. An *ocular micrometer* is now placed on the eyepiece diaphragm, and its image thus appears to lie upon that of the stage micrometer. The ocular micrometer is a thick, circular glass, with a finely ruled scale whose lines are matched with those of the stage micrometer so that the values of the lines in the ocular may be determined. Since this scale is magnified by the eye lens and projected as a virtual image, it is necessary to calibrate its dimensions by means of the stage micrometer for every combination of eyepiece and objective. Once this has been done, a record is made and the computations do not have to be repeated. When the stage micrometer is removed and an object slide mounted, the eyepiece scale is projected as part of the virtual image, and direct readings of sizes of parts are made. When this figure is multiplied by the calibration factor, the actual size is obtained.

For rough outline drawing, practice the method known as *double vision*. The setup consists of a pile of large magazines, a sheet of drawing paper, and a well-sharpened drawing pencil. Stack the magazines against the right side of the microscope until their upper surface is 10 inches below the eyepoint of the instrument and thus in the plane of the virtual image. The microscope should be vertical and the illumination uniform over both the magazines and the microscope mirror. Such lighting is best achieved by using a fluorescent table lamp. Place the sheet of drawing paper on top of the magazines and choose a slide that has some large-scale detail, such as a section of a vertebrate organ.

Looking through the tube with the left eye, take up the pencil with the right hand and move it slowly about over the paper, starting near the microscope pillar. If the eyes are accommodated at infinity and no conscious attempt is made to see the pencil, it should appear, wandering around among the tissues. As long as the vision can be kept in this condition the pencil point can be seen, and outlines of major features can be traced, but as soon as any effort is made to concentrate on the pencil—a perfectly natural effort—it disappears.

An accessory instrument for drawing is the *camera lucida*. There are several designs, but the Abbe model is preferred. It consists of a cap that fits over the microscope eyepiece, housing a prism and a series of apertures containing tinted glasses arranged in a scale of increasing darkness. A mirror on an arm at the right is so turned that it reflects an image of the pencil point on the drawing paper to a silvered prism and thence to the eye. At the same time the eye also scans the object through a hole in the silvering of the prism. The smoked glasses make it possible to balance the illumination of the two superposed images—the object and the pencil—thus increasing sharpness. The operator now has only to trace what he sees.

Easiest to use is some form of *microprojector* (Fig. 31). This instrument is a member of the microscope family arranged to throw a real image of the object upon a large sheet of cloth or paper on the wall, for tracing in the making of charts, or on an ordinary sheet of paper on the table top for smaller reproductions, as in illustrating a scientific article. It is widely used in schools and colleges for teaching and quizzing, and is obtainable in many styles, sizes, and prices. The microscopist who has some facility with tools can readily make his own microprojector.

Photomicrography, or the art of taking photographs through a microscope, is not at all difficult, though to become an expert

Fig. 31. Leitz research microscope Ortholux; composite photograph showing attachments for drawing and projection.

you must have long experience and develop more than average skill, as in any other form of photography. The *photomicrographic camera* (Fig. 58) need be no more than a light tight box, painted black on the inside, with an aperture at one end to fit over the microscope eyepiece, and a plate or film holder at the other. The many professional models are but elaborations of this design. No shutter is necessary, since exposures may be made by turning the microscope lamp on and off. No camera lens is used, the microscope providing the means for focusing the image on the ground glass. The apparatus may be set up either vertically, as when live material is the object on the stage, or horizontally. An old view or portrait camera, minus the lens and shutter, and with a long bellows extension, is ideal.

In making pictures, a series of exposures of increasing length is obtained, and results are compared. A longer exposure will be required if one changes from a lower to a higher magnification, and if the object is more deeply stained or is thicker or more opaque. Soon the operator achieves a fairly good idea of just how long an exposure is needed for each new object. He then begins to experiment with color filters, described earlier in this chapter. He makes an exposure of the same subject and same duration for each of several differently colored filters interposed between light source and microscope, and compares results. Motion pictures can be made of moving objects, such as protozoans, following the same principles. Either still or motion pictures may be made when using the special techniques previously described: dark-field, ultraviolet, polarized-light, phase-contrast. Still pictures of the images formed by the electron microscope are termed electron micrographs.

Some sources for scientific instruments and apparatus, glassware, and reagents

A. S. Aloe Co., 1831 Olive St., St. Louis 3, Mo.
Central Scientific Co. (Cenco), 1700 Irving Park Rd., Chicago 13. Ill.
Chicago Apparatus Co., 1735 N. Ashland Ave., Chicago 22, Ill.
Clay-Adams Co., Inc., 141 E. 25th St., New York 10, N.Y.
A. Daigger & Co., Kinzie & Wells Sts., Chicago 10, Ill.
Fisher Scientific Co., 717 Forbes St., Pittsburgh 19, Pa.

Phipps & Bird, Inc., Richmond, Va.

E. H. Sargent & Co., 155 E. Superior St., Chicago, Ill.

Schaar & Co., 7300 W. Montrose Ave., Chicago 34, Ill.

Scientific Laboratory Supply Co., 139 Forrest Ave., N.E., Atlanta, Ga.

Standard Scientific Supply Corp., 34 W. 4th St., New York 12, N.Y.

Arthur H. Thomas Co., W. Washington Sq., Philadelphia 5, Pa.

United Scientific Co., 200 N. Jefferson St., Chicago 6, Ill.

W. M. Welch Scientific Co., 1515 Sedgwick St., Chicago 10, Ill.

Will Corporation, Rochester 3, N.Y.

chapter five

The microcosm

Having completed an introductory survey of the microscope, its operation, and its accessories, we are now ready to embark on the first of numerous adventures in the world of little things. The ancients had no conception of many forms of matter that today are well understood. The universe evident to the naked eye—without the aid of either microscope to discover objects too small or telescope with which to observe things too distant —was their cosmos, their known total of matter. The term *microcosm* is therefore a most appropriate one for the world of life revealed to us by means of microscopes.

In a single drop of water the microscopist may watch numbers of strange creatures engaged in the same eternal struggle that is enacted in the jungle, where the tiger strikes down the deer; on the mountain, where wolf trails rabbit; in the apparently peaceful meadow, where garter snake seizes mouse; and in the depths of the sea, where the shark leaves a trail of blood. The struggle to preserve one's own life—to eat but not to be eaten—and the urge to reproduce: these are the two great necessities of all forms of life, great or small, and they are just as pressing among the inhabitants of the microcosm as in the larger world with which all of us are familiar.

Collecting microcosmic materials

For this adventure we shall need to outfit ourselves properly before our descent into the microcosm. We must stalk formidable beasts, invade their lairs, and carry them off as captives to our worktable. If you don't think they're formidable—well, wait till we place ourselves in the position of one of their intended victims, imagining that we are only a thousandth part of an inch in height! If a *Stylonychia* came charging down upon us then—we would think him even more terrifying than his name sounds to us now!

We will need several vessels for the cultures to be collected and reared. A few pint and quart fruit jars are as useful as any type, though the cylindrical kind of glass receptacle known as a *battery jar* makes an inexpensive and much better looking and more transparent aquarium. Small fish globes and kitchen jars are now widely available in the ten-cent stores. A *collecting bag* of one sort or other is highly useful in the field. The armed forces surplus stores retail a very modestly priced knapsack, and camping outfits generally include similar items. A few *pipettes*—the laboratory term for the ordinary medicine dropper—and some *gummed labels* complete the present equipment.

COLLECTING   The kinds of organisms that can be collected will depend on the part of the world in which you live, the immediate surroundings, whether city or country, and the season of the year. This is less true for microorganisms, however, than for those of the visible world. The following are suggestions: make as many of these collections as your locality and opportunities allow. You will have a lot of fun in making all of them.

1. Collect microorganisms from fresh-water localities. Wide-mouthed bottles of 2-oz. capacity are best for this work, though any similar receptacles will serve. Find a pond in the fields or a city park, backwater eddy adjacent to a stream, roadside pool or ditch, or any small body of more or less stagnant water in which there are aquatic plants, fallen leaves, or scum. If any water-lily pads are available so much the better.

Collecting bottles to be used must be thoroughly clean and free from any traces of former contents, such as drugs, that might poison the delicate pond inhabitants they are now to contain. Immerse a bottle beneath the water with the cork in place, and work it into position so that when the cork is removed and water rushes in, the flow will carry in muck, mud, decaying leaves, or other organic detritus. You can also push in these things with your fingers. Cork the bottle before removing it. The filled container should have no more than one-fifth of its volume in the form of solid matter—the rest water. Label as to locality, kind of aquatic situation, and the date, then place in the haversack.

Make similar collections from various localities and types of water, labeling each. Cut bits of lily pads and place them in a separate bottle, filled with the water in which they were growing. Collect the visible kinds of algae, always with much more water than plant material. Collect from brackish water and from salt water also, as opportunity offers. Scrapings from the larger seaweeds, as *Fucus*, the rockweed, will be rewarding.

2. Make or buy a *plankton net* for collecting in the larger bodies of water, such as ocean bays, rivers, and lakes. The net may be towed from a boat, the speed of which is just fast enough to keep the net at the surface, or fastened to a line at the end of a long bamboo fishing pole, the operator walking along the shore as he trolls the net, or casting it so as to retrieve it via the best-looking collecting areas. When the catch is judged sufficient, it is spilled into a finger bowl and samples are inspected under the microscope. The *biological finger bowls*, obtainable from supply houses, are most useful items of laboratory glassware; they stack one on another, each forming a lid for the one below. A similar article is available at dime stores.

3. Collect trash from the bottoms of old urns that may sometimes be found in gardens or on gateposts. If there is water in the bottom of the urn, include some of it—otherwise gather dry material, making a culture as directed in item 7 below.

4. Some interesting material may be obtained from an aquarium if one is available to you in the home or school. The ordinary goldfish globe is too small and clean, but the balanced, covered aquarium will include a wealth of microorganisms. With a safety-razor blade scrape off some of the green scum from the glass sides and cut off small pieces of some of

the growing plants, placing them in bottles with some of the surrounding water.

You may find tiny green or brown threads, about ⅛ to ¼ in. in length, attached by one end to the glass side of the aquarium nearest the light. The other end waves about and has a crown of minute tentacles, or arms. This creature is *Hydra*, a famous animal, biologically speaking. They may be scraped off or sucked into a pipette, but they must be expelled immediately into a watch glass, as they are quick to anchor inside the pipette and then are the dickens to dislodge. In nature they occur in the same sort of situation described in item 1, lily pads being a favorite collecting site. The small container chiefly used for animals of this minute bulk is the *Syracuse watch glass*. These glasses stack, they may be placed on the stage of a microscope, and they have a ground flange which can be written on with a pencil, for labeling the temporary contents. The glass furniture glider from the ten-cent store is an inferior but acceptable substitute.

5. Take advantage of any institutions or organizations in your locality that might provide special materials; a fish hatchery, for example, can supply microcrustacea.

6. Capture one or more frogs of any species and bring them alive to your laboratory. They must be kept cool and moist but should not be immersed in water. A frog may be kept for some time in a coffee can, with holes punched in the sides, near the top, to admit air, and with daily attention to moisture —a spoonful of water in the bottom is enough. Feed the frog on earthworms, and keep the can clean and cool. Larger collections can be maintained similarly in a bucket.

Perhaps you will wish to make a *terrarium*, the land-environment equivalent of the aquarium. For this purpose, a rectangular aquarium is best, such as the 10- by 20-in. size, or larger. Prop one end up on a cleat so that the floor slopes, maintain a pool of water in the lower third or fourth portion, and pave the remainder with moss, peat, muck, or soil. Plant ferns and appropriate native flowering species; to make a varied environment, put in a small log, dead leaves, a few stones; stock with selections of frogs, salamanders, small turtles and snakes, land snails, earthworms, ground-dwelling insects and spiders. But do not overstock. A glass plate as a lid will maintain proper humidity within the terrarium.

7. Begin the culture of the microcosm known as the *hay infusion*. To do this, first draw off a battery jar or 2-qt. fruit jar full of water from the cold-water tap and allow it to stand uncovered for three days so that excess oxygen dissolved in the water will evaporate. Too much oxygen in the water is injurious or fatal to the organisms to be cultured. Mark the water level by pasting a small label on the outside of the jar so that its top edge is flush with the level; this is so that additional water may be added from time to time to maintain this level. Remember to add only water that has stood for awhile, like the first jarful. Then add a handful of pieces of dry hay, cut into short lengths. Any type or mixture of dried grasses may be used, but timothy is preferred. Cover the jar and stand it where it will receive daylight but not direct sunlight. The cover may be round or square and cut from any glass scrap.

The variety of life that will develop from these wisps of hay is astounding. In a later chapter we shall follow through the cycles of dominant forms and tell you where these animals and plants come from and what happens to them.

8. In a fingerbowl, and in the same way described in item 7, begin the lettuce microcosm by adding some bits of scrap lettuce to water.

Temporary wet mounts

Back in the laboratory again, after a collecting trip, the first necessity is to take care of our captives. Line the bottles up on the table and replace the cork of each with a square of gauze (cheesecloth), of such size that it may lie flat across the bottle top and be gathered around the neck, where it is held by a rubber band. Stand a clean pipette vertically beside each bottle and bind the two together with a second rubber band. The reasons for these steps are not far to seek: cultures and collections must breathe, so we punch holes in the can for the frog, and replace the cork with gauze for ameba and his cohorts. Each bottle and jar must have its own pipette so that it will not be contaminated by another. You may label the pipettes to correspond with the bottles, or give each set a distinctive number or color. Soft wax pencils for such uses are called glass-writing pencils. The rubber band system is simplest and will be sufficient if the operator is methodical and careful.

Add more water to each bottle from time to time. Generally the proper level is indicated by a ring of scum on the inside, marking the original height; or use labels. The best water is that from which the collection was made, but if it is not readily obtainable, keep a stock bottle of oxygen-depleted tap water for this purpose.

Slides and covers should be entirely clean before being used. Wash them in water to which some detergent has been added, and dry with soft cloths. Handle them only by the edges, and avoid touching the flat surfaces thereafter. Store clean glassware in a clean receptacle, covered to exclude dust. Small glass or plastic boxes are suggested; for example, some brands of typewritter ribbons now come in a clear plastic circular box with slipover or pillbox type of lid, ideal for storing cover glasses.

Slides may be dried as you would dry any glassware, but covers offer a problem because of their extreme fragility. Two methods are in favor. First, cover the right hand with a soft, clean handkerchief and grasp a cover glass by its flat surfaces, the cloth intervening between glass and skin. Move the thumb and forefinger back and forth, pressing on the cover glass between them; this cleans without breaking since the pressure on both sides of the cover is equalized. Second, hold the cover by its edges between the thumb and forefinger of the left hand; rub back and forth with the cloth-covered thumb and first finger of the right hand. This method requires a bit more practice to avoid breakage, but it gives the best results. Hold the cover glass to the light and examine it; if it is not thoroughly clean, breathe on both sides in quick succession and repeat the polishing. Some microscopists like to polish covers between two small hardwood blocks, perfectly flat and covered with chamois.

To clean pipettes, remove the rubber bulb and squeeze it shut and open several times vigorously in water to flush it well. Hold the glass barrel in the flowing stream from the tap, and run a pipe cleaner through it. Allow the parts to dry by themselves in a dust-free place, or dry them in an incubator.

Place a clean slide flat upon the table before you and have a clean cover at hand, so located that it may be picked up quickly when wanted. There are several ways of making sure that you can pick up the cover quickly. The cover may be placed on the stage of the microscope, projecting from one corner enough so that it may be grasped; a safety-match box stood vertically on the table makes an excellent mound from which to retrieve a cover; the cover may be leaned against any convenient object at an angle; or it may be held in a *cover-glass forceps* (Fig. 34), a gadget so designed as to work in reverse, releasing objects when the halves are pressed together.

With a pipette remove a small portion of water and scum or sediment from the surface of the solid contents of a collection bottle—the bottom water level, where sediment and water meet. Place 2 drops of this mixture upon the center of the slide, seeing that some of the debris is included, but without any thick or elevated masses that would interfere with the cover. Nine-tenths or more of these drops should be water.

For hand mounting, grasp a cover by its edges and bring it over the slide. Lower it so that one edge touches the slide, just beyond the culture. Figure 32 shows the correct position. Then merely let go and allow the cover to fall gently upon the culture, whereupon the fluid will immediately spread out into an even film beneath the cover. If the correct amount of culture has been taken, the cover will float upon the liquid, but with no excess to run out from beneath. A little experience will show just the right amount to use; less with thin mixtures, more with thicker ones. Under no circumstances allow any fluid to get on the top surface of the cover; if this happens, clean up the slide and cover and start over. A second method of mounting is to hold the cover at an angle over the culture, as before, then with a dissecting needle prop the upper edge of the cover

Fig. 32. Adding cover glass with the fingers.

(Fig. 33), and lower this glass gently upon the culture. This method is the same as the first except that it is more gradual and gentle. A third procedure, preferred by many, is to employ the cover-glass forceps: again let one edge of the cover touch the slide, lower the cover carefully, and let go with the forceps (Fig. 34).

Now with the instrument vertical, not inclined, mount your slide on the stage of the microscope. Observe precautions as to clips. It is best either to remove them or swing them back to the rear so that they are not in use at all. If you prefer to have their aid in maintaining the slide in place, take care while moving the slide about that neither clip comes in contact with the edge of the cover. If it does so it will draw out some of the culture from beneath the cover, by capillarity, taking away too much of your study material, as well as smearing water over slide and stage.

Secure a focus with a moderate amount of light. Most of the organisms to be observed are more or less transparent, and too bright a light will render them well-nigh invisible. Experiment a bit with the different intensities of illumination, and decide on the range that is best for your eyes.

This form of slide preparation is a temporary wet mount. It is not intended to last very long, and both the slides and

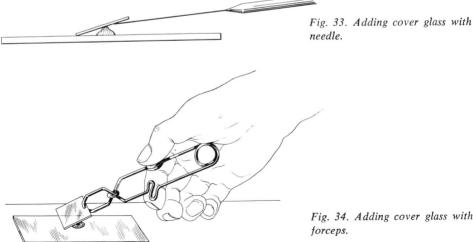

Fig. 33. Adding cover glass with needle.

Fig. 34. Adding cover glass with forceps.

72

covers should be rinsed, dried, and stored for future use. Permanent and stained mounts of unicellular organisms are a bit too difficult so early in the game. The making of such slides will be taken up in Chapter 11.

And here, then, before us is the invisible world of tiny creatures, far smaller and more wondrous than Gulliver's people of Lilliput. These are creatures of strange shapes, queer structures, variety of motion—some will be stationary, others moving about slowly, and still others dashing hither and yon in a mad and apparently aimless scurrying. In the next chapter we are going to tell you about various methods of studying and controlling these organisms, help you identify many of them, suggest varying procedures for the different cultures, and give you some pointers on classification and the modes of life among the Protozoa.

As to just what results you will obtain from this first peep into the microcosm, it is impossible for us to say. Some cultures prepared with the best of care will show scarcely anything, others will be exceedingly rich in living material. Most of these organisms are world-wide in distribution, but they have their ranges and their haunts, as do their big brothers of the familiar world of animals. You will not find goats in the ocean nor swallows in the barn in the wintertime. Nevertheless, if you have collected from several different kinds of localities, you may be certain of good results with at least some.

Some principal biological supply houses

Cambosco Scientific Co., 37 Antwerp St., Boston, Mass.

Carolina Biological Supply Co., Elon College, N.C.

Geo. H. Conant, Triarch Botanical Products, Ripon, Wis.

Denoyer-Geppert Co., 5235 Ravenswood Ave., Chicago 40, Ill.

Flatters & Garnett, Ltd., 309, Oxford Rd., Manchester 13, England.

Albert E. Galigher, Inc., Box 63, Albany Station, Berkeley, Calif. Prepared microscope slides.

General Biological Supply House, Inc., 8200 S. Hoyne Ave., Chicago 20, Ill.

The Lemberger Co., 1436 S. Park Ave., Oshkosh, Wis. Live animals.

Marine Biological Laboratory, Supply Dept., Woods Hole, Mass.

New York Scientific Supply Co. (Nyssco), 28 W. 30th St., New York 1, N.Y.

Powers & Powers, P.O. Box 312, Denver 1, Colo. Prepared microscope slides.

Quivira Specialties Co., 4204 W. 21st St., Topeka, Kan.

J. R. Schettle Frog Farm, Route 1, Stillwater, Minn. Live animals.

Southwestern Biological Supply Co., P.O. Box 4084, Dallas, Tex.

Standard Zoological Products Co., 11 W. 42d St., New York, N.Y.

E. G. Steinhilber & Co., Oshkosh, Wis. Live animals.

William Tricker, Inc., Independence, Ohio. Aquarium supplies.

Ward's Natural Science Establishment, Inc., 3000 Ridge Rd. E., Rochester 9, N.Y.

chapter six

The protozoa

With our cultures collected and microcosms under way, we may now discuss what sort of information is to be gained from them. In the usual aquatic collection, at the microscopic level, there should be numerous small animals: hydra, worms, rotifers, microcrustacea, and others of the multicellular animals that make up the higher divisions of the animal kingdom. But the bulk of the organisms collected will be protozoans, the single-celled creatures that are not green in color and that will be seen in motion. There will be one-celled plants, representing the algae, some of which are also found as colonies of cells, arranged in strands or spheres. Some of the material seen will be dead organisms, empty casings, bits of soil, crystals, and unrecognizable debris.

Care of temporary mounts

In the preceding chapter the method of making temporary wet mounts was described. There are certain additional points to which we should now turn our attention.

EVAPORATION   As soon as a fresh mount is prepared, evaporation of the water sets in. Of course it is slow, for the water is exposed to air only at the edges of the cover glass. If evaporation is not prevented, the average slide will dry out in about thirty minutes. If this length of time will suffice for the observation you have in mind, well and good. It is better practice, however, to prevent culture slides from becoming dry. Drying draws the cover down ever more tightly to the slide, crushing and finally killing all the organisms present. A completely dry slide is more difficult to clean for later use.

To maintain a slide in working condition, a drop of the same culture as that on the slide should be added every fifteen minutes or so, as appearances seem to indicate. Using great care, allow this drop to fall from the pipette, held very close to the slide, just at the edge of the cover glass. If this is properly done, no liquid should get on the top of the cover. If contact is made with the water under the cover, the added water will be drawn under by capillarity and will restore the quantity of liquid under the cover without getting any of it *on* the cover.

STAINING Various chemicals used to color objects in a slide of this character may be added in the same manner—by placing a drop just at the margin of the cover. The stain will diffuse through the water beneath the cover and gradually tint the various organisms present. An *intra-vitam* dye will stain without injuring the organism. Most dyes contain mineral acids and their salts and are lethal, i.e., they will poison and kill the microorganisms. Iodine and Mercurochrome, among stains that we shall use, are examples. Neutral red is a commonly used intra-vitam dye. Make a 1 per cent solution of neutral red in distilled water (1-gm. dry stain to 100 cc. water), then add just 1 drop of this *stock solution* to a tumblerful of distilled water. This makes an extremely dilute solution in which no red color is apparent to the eye, yet when it is added to a slide, the dye content is sufficient to stain all the organisms red.

Whenever it is desired to *replace* one fluid with another, without removing the cover glass (which ruins the preparation), add the second liquid as before and, with torn-off bits of filter paper or toweling, draw out the first fluid from the opposite side; one is drawn off from the left side as the second enters from the right.

Rough-and-ready stains that you may try at this time, in addition to neutral red, are fountain-pen ink, Mercurochrome,

76

Merthiolate, tincture of iodine, and any water-color pigments that might be at hand.

SEALING It is frequently desirable to maintain a fresh mount for several hours or longer without causing disturbance by adding new fluid. When the new liquid is run under the cover, currents are set up that will be likely to sweep away a particular cell you might have under observation, and you may never succeed in finding it again. This point may loom as highly important if you are watching one of the fascinating events in Microland, such as the division of a living cell or the engulfing of one cell by another. To avoid this disturbing event, seal the cover glass to the slide with petroleum jelly.

Make a petroleum-jelly gun as follows: remove the rubber bulb from a pipette; place small quantities of petroleum jelly in the bulb end of the glass barrel, using a toothpick as applicator. Every so often, pound the small end of the tube upon the table or any smooth wooden surface, hard enough to jar the petroleum jelly down into the tube but not so hard as to break the glass. Keep this up, slowly and patiently, until the barrel is full; the idea of the pounding is to let trapped air escape. Use a glass rod, match stick, or whittled stick as a plunger and, when all is ready, force out a steady cylinder of petroleum jelly as you move the gun along a slide, sealing it against evaporation. In this connection, look up "turntable" in the index and read instructions on how it can be used with a circular cover glass.

SPECIAL SLIDES Widely used for special purposes are *depression slides*, with one, two, or three concavities ground into the surface of a slide that is a trifle thicker than ordinary. Figure 35 indicates how a small drop of culture can be placed on a cover glass, which is then inverted over the cavity of a depression slide. This makes a *hanging-drop suspension* and provides a quantity of water, limited by its own film, in which the microorganisms can move about. Of course the whole depression can be filled, and either preparation can be sealed or not, as desired. A much thicker slab of glass is the *deep-well slide*,

Fig. 35. Depression slide with hanging drop.

having a circular depression with vertical sides. This is rather deep for protozoa, which would be diving, rising, and continually going out of focus, but is excellent for somewhat larger organisms. The Pyrex spot plate is the latest slide of this type.

QUIETING Many of our subjects will be found to swim so actively that observation under high power is impossible without some method of interfering with or controlling their locomotion. Each organism should be studied first under low power, to gain knowledge of its movements and habits, then under high power for structural details. Here are some of the ways in which various investigators have slowed down the swifter protozoans for high-power studies:

Entrapment. Fray out a tiny bit of cotton so as to make an exceedingly thin mat and place this on a slide. Add the culture and a cover glass. This makes a forest of fibers that trap the organisms and interfere with their activities—but it also interferes with your view of them.

Impeding. To a drop of culture on a slide add 1 drop of a 10 per cent solution of fully hydrolyzed polyvinyl alcohol, or 1 drop of methyl cellulose. Mix thoroughly with a pin or toothpick, and add a cover. The protozoans are slowed down immediately, becoming practically stationary, but they are not distorted and their structure is readily studied under high power. Another recommended procedure is to make a ring of the quieting medium on the slide, place the drop of culture fluid in the center, and cover. The quieter will diffuse slowly into the culture. At first the organisms are fully active, but they gradually slow down, and you may thus observe them first in the unimpeded condition and later when they have been stopped. By either method these slides will last several hours, since evaporation is retarded.[2]

Feeding. Some of the most active protozoans, like *Paramecium,* that swim about so rapidly as to defy study under high power can be concentrated and quieted in one place by feeding. Mash up a tiny speck of yeast cake in a drop of water and place this in the center of the area to be covered; add culture and cover glass. The yeast-feeding protozoans will soon

[2] Both these quieters are obtainable in 1-oz. bottles or in larger quantities, ready to use, from the Carolina Biological Supply Co., Elon College, N.C.

78

congregate about this microscopic dining table, and here and there will be one that remains so motionless that he can be kept continuously in view under a 43× objective. If a drop of the neutral red solution is also added when this slide is made up, the process of ingestion of food, and its subsequent course, may be studied.

Anesthetizing, Narcotizing. The principle of using a drug can be applied to protozoa as well as to larger animals. Among those that have been used successfully are a 1 per cent solution of magnesium sulfate or magnesium chloride, and a 0.1 per cent solution of nicotine. If you have access to a sleeping pill, try a 1:1,000 dilution (1,000 parts of water to 1 of the pill). Pantin recommends inverting a drop on a slide over the mouth of a small bottle that contains tobacco smoke for fifteen seconds to one minute. Then remove the slide, add more water if desired, and a cover glass.

Drying. The simplest procedure of all is to let nature take its course and allow the slide to dry by evaporation. As the water is lost, the cover is drawn down ever more closely upon the organisms, and there is a brief interval, before they are crushed, during which their activities are greatly restricted and when high-power observations may easily be made. There will be some distortion as to shape, but good detail of internal structures may be seen.

The classes of protozoa

The single-celled animals constitute one of the major groups (phyla) of the animal kingdom and are in turn divided into four classes on a basis of the form taken by the structures that produce locomotion. One class is wholly parasitic, and all of them contain at least a few parasitic species, some of which are very important as causative agents of diseases in man and domestic animals.

CLASS MASTIGOPHORA (whip bearers) The cell is provided with one or more long, slender, threadlike or whiplike processes, whose lashings propel the animal. Some swim through the field very rapidly and must be quieted; others are slow. Most are independent, but some are colonial—clusters of cells living together and acting as if they were a many-celled or-

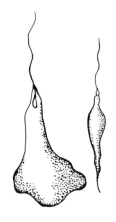

ganism. The whiplash is called a *flagellum*, and those creatures that have them are *flagellates*. They are very small as compared with other protozoans that you will see in your cultures.

Peranema (Fig. 36) is a species that you are likely to encounter. It is one of the slower types and spends much of its time in changing shape, as it is very plastic. There are two flagellums, though one is trailing and small, difficult to observe. The evident one is long and large but will puzzle the observer in that it seems to be stationary even while the animal is moving forward; this is because only the tip of the little whip is vibrating, and this may be seen only with high power and a dim light. The dark-field and phase-contrast techniques are of course excellent for this purpose.

Astasia (Fig. 36) also has two flagellums, one trailing and seldom seen, the other large, long, and in active motion. The cell is pear-shaped, narrow in front, wider posteriorly. It moves ahead with a slow and steady progression and makes an ideal type for study. *Euglena* will be discussed with the algae. It is claimed by both botanists and zoologists, as it has some characteristics of an animal nature, others that are plantlike.

Among parasitic flagellates may be cited the genus *Trypanosoma* (Fig. 36), which includes some of the worst enemies of man in the tropics. *T. gambiense* is the pathogen, or disease causer, of Gambian sleeping sickness in West Africa, and *T. rhodesiense* is the organism that produces the very similar Rhodesian sleeping sickness. The carriers are tsetse flies, which transmit these blood parasites from antelope to man. There are many other species, the one most commonly studied in laboratories in the United States being *T. lewisi*, a rat parasite with a flea carrier. Here we have a symptomless case, unlike the deadly reactions in man, the infection soon dying out, without harm to the rat. Prepared slides, living cultures, or infected rats may be purchased from supply houses.

Fortunately for the novice, however, there is a much simpler way of getting a look at a living trypanosome under his microscope. In the blood of the common newt (*Triturus*), an aquatic salamander found throughout most of the United States, one of these parasites, *T. diemictyli*, is of common occurrence, while *T. rotatorium* is found in many frogs, the intermediate host being a leech. The newt species looks much

Fig. 36. Flagellates. From top: Peranema *contracted and* Peranema *extended;* Astasia; Trypanosoma.

like the ones found in mammals, while the frog parasite is larger and stouter; but either one will give the uninitiated a thrill when he first sees specimens swimming about among blood corpuscles and realizes that he is observing the same type of organism that causes a fatal disease in man.

A number of flagellates occur in the human mouth, intestine, and urogenital tract. Of these *Giardia intestinalis (lamblia)* is probably the most serious, though none of them are considered very dangerous.

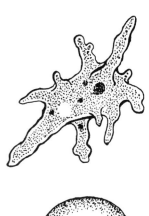

CLASS SARCODINA   The type form for study is the famous ameba (Fig. 37), which may appear in some of your lily-pad collections; if not, a small bottle containing a dozen or so may be purchased from any biological supply house. This is a creeping organism and is to be sought crawling along on the surface of sediment from the bottom of your jars or on the larger fragments of lily leaves. Cut down the light when making examinations and look for an irregular bit of nearly transparent jelly. The rude shock to the amebas of being sucked up into a pipette and forcefully deposited on a slide results in a brief period of inactivity, so give them a little time to recover. Then watch one as it protrudes *pseudopodia* (false feet), which are temporary projections into which the cell substance streams. New pseudopods form at whatever surface of the animal happens to be moving forward at the time, and this flowing should be watched under high power. Here is *protoplasm*, the primary life stuff, in one of its simplest and most readily available forms. You may see an ameba contrive a food cup and engulf some other cell, or watch one as it flows around some object that interferes with its forward progression.

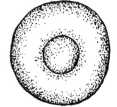

Arcella (Fig. 37) resembles a doughnut in front view, a football from the side, having a brown shell with a circular opening in the lower surface through which pseudopodia are put forth. This species and *Difflugia* (Fig. 37) are shelled amebas, the latter having a case made of sand grains and diatom shells cemented together in the shape of a helmet.

Five kinds of amebas occur in the human intestinal tract, all more or less associated with diarrhea, but the only one of major importance is *Endamoeba histolytica* (Fig. 37), patho-

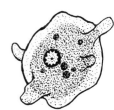

Fig. 37. Sarcodina.
From top: Amoeba proteus; Arcella; Difflugia; Endamoeba histolytica.

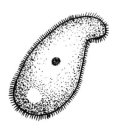

gen of bloody, or amebic, dysentery. Infection is direct, through unsanitary personal habits, and there is no intermediate host. In the feeding stage, this ameba ingests red corpuscles and makes dangerous ulcers; it may invade the liver. In the inactive cyst stage it passes out of the host with the feces and is the source of infection of new hosts in contaminated food and drink. The incidence of infestation is very high throughout the world, including the whole of the United States, and the mortality is also high. *Endamoeba* is coming to be regarded as one of the worst of all protozoan enemies of mankind. There is a common species available for study in the colon of the cockroach, *E. blattae*, and another, *E. invadens*, from snakes and turtles, that will give the student a good idea of a parasitic ameba. Material for the making of smear slides of *E. histolytica* may be obtained from medical laboratories, and prepared slides of the trophozoite (feeding) stage or cyst stage may be purchased from supply houses.

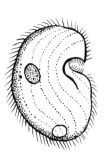

CLASS SPOROZOA   This is a class in which the adult members do not move and in which all are parasites. They are usually minute and, being motionless, are not spectacular in the living state, but nevertheless they interest us because of their harmful and often disastrous effects on the tissues of their hosts. The malarial organism is a member of this group; we shall refer to it again when the preparation of blood smears is discussed.

CLASS CILIOPHORA   The great majority, the largest, and the most active and interesting of all those protozoans met with in the average culture belong to the Ciliophora (cilia bearers), formerly termed the Infusoria. The characteristic structure, the *cilium* (eyelash), is a short, hairlike process, generally very numerous, and those protozoans that have them are termed *ciliates*. By means of rapid waves of contraction that lash the cilia backward, ciliates swim at a high speed; they must be impeded for high-power observations.

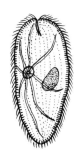

Fig. 38. Ciliates; holotrichs. From top: Paramecium; Colpidium; Colpoda; Frontonia; Didinium.

Paramecium (Fig. 38) is the type form, studied in all biology courses, and should occur in many of your collections. This cell is just at the limit of visibility of the unaided eye. If a watch glass containing a number of them is placed on a black background and strongly illuminated from above, the paramecia may be seen as tiny whitish specks swimming about. The cell is slipper-shaped, bluntly rounded at the front end, constricted at the middle, becoming widest past the middle, then tapering to the posterior end, not quite so blunt as the anterior. Under low power you will note that the animal rotates as it moves and at certain angles appears somewhat flattened. There is a large spirally directed oral groove running from the forward end to a point just to the rear of the middle of the body, where it terminates in the mouth. Food particles, mainly bacteria, are scooped up by the groove, which narrows and deepens toward the mouth, and then are forced down a short gullet into the interior of the cell, where they are collected with a bit of water in a small ball that breaks off and goes floating away inside the cell as a food vacuole. A rapidly vibrating membrane in the gullet, consisting of fused cilia, assists in this performance. Digestive fluids secreted by the paramecium are sent into the food vacuoles, and as these circle around within the animal, the food particles are digested. If some finely ground bits of carmine are added to the water when the slide is made, paramecium will ingest these bright red grains and the whole performance may be watched from start to finish. Rouge is a readily available form of carmine.

Another structure of great interest in protozoans is the contractile vacuole. Ameba has one, paramecium two, one near each end. These vacuoles periodically fill with wastes, move to the surface, and expel their contents to the exterior. They look like small bubbles that increase in size and then burst, disappearing instantly, only to reappear later. The contractile vacuoles of paramecium are filled through a series of radiating

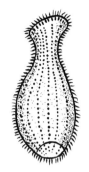

Fig. 39. Ciliates; holotrichs. From top: Spathidium; Coleps; Lacrymaria; Dileptus.

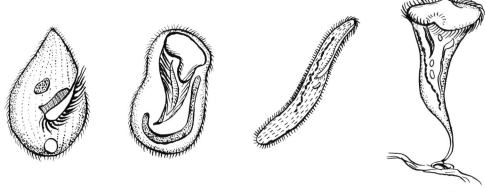

Fig. 40. Ciliates; heterotrichs. From left: Blepharisma; Bursaria; Spirostomum; Stentor.

canals, and they beat rhythmically but alternately; the anterior vacuole is being filled when the posterior is empty.

Paramecium is covered all over by cilia that are more or less uniform in length; such ciliates are termed *holotrichs*. Some other members of this group (Figs. 38, 39) are *Colpidium,* about the size of a paramecium but with the anterior end permanently bent at an angle, often appearing in immense numbers in a hay infusion; *Colpoda,* small, kidney-shaped, has the mouth notched in the concave side; *Frontonia* is like a large, robust paramecium without a middle constriction; *Didinium,* the paramecium tiger, looks like a miniature turtle and, though smaller than its victims, preys on paramecia, sucking them into its terminal mouth and swallowing them whole; *Spathidium,* medium to large, with a terminal mouth and vase-shaped body, also is a predator; *Coleps,* barrel-shaped and medium in size, with a terminal mouth, appears to be armor-clad, with numerous plates arranged in a geometric pattern; *Lacrymaria,* the swan animal, is very large, with a mouth at the apex and a long "neck," which can be thrashed about vigorously; and *Dileptus,* another large protozoan, also has a long "neck," but the mouth is at its base, not at the apex as in *Lacrymaria.*

Heterotrichs (Fig. 40) are those ciliates that possess cilia all over the body and have in addition, in a zone near the mouth, rows of fused cilia (membranelles), arranged one behind another like little paddles, which serve to propel food particles toward the mouth. A few of the best-known types are *Blepharisma*, which has somewhat the size and shape of a paramecium but will astonish you because it is pink in color; *Spirostomum*, pencil-shaped, long and straight, with one huge rear contractile vacuole—a veritable giant among the Protozoa, attaining a length of 3 mm., but capable of contracting to a remarkable degree; *Bursaria*, the purse animal, very large and vase-shaped, highly carnivorous, devouring many paramecia; and *Stentor*, the trumpet animal, dark blue in color and also very large, usually attached to some object but capable of breaking off and swimming rapidly away.

Hypotrichs (Fig. 41) usually have, in addition to a mouth zone of membranelles, a number of ventral cirri. Cirri are tufts of cilia that fuse so as to make a fairly stiff structure, used as a leg; a protozoan so equipped runs rapidly over a surface. *Stylonychia*, the best-known hypotrich, reminds one of a microscopic bug as it scampers along on the surface of the slide or on a strand of alga. The bottom surface of the animal is flat, the top arched, the shape somewhat oval but wider posteriorly; the size is that of a paramecium, smaller in some species. Characteristic are three caudal (tail) cirri, which project as bristles. *Oxytrichia* is similar but lacks these caudal cirri. *Euplotes* is shorter, smaller, and rounder, and the cirri are very large. *Uroleptus* is elongate and has the bottom cirri in rows.

Oligotrichs are the least abundant of ciliates. They have the

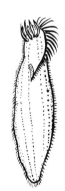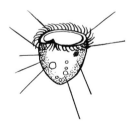

Fig. 41. Ciliates; hypotrichs. From left: **Stylonychia**; Uroleptus; Euplotes; *an oligotrich,* **Halteria.**

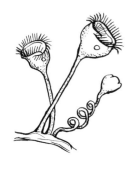

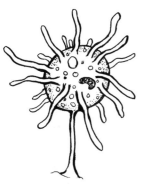

Fig. 42. Ciliates; peritrichs.
From top: Vorticella;
Epistylis; *a suctorean,*
Podophyra.

same mouth zone as the heterotrichs and hypotrichs, but the ciliation elsewhere on the body is greatly reduced or absent. The only form likely to be encountered is *Halteria* (Fig. 41), which has a belt of cirri around the middle. This cell is small and roundish, but the principal feature that will at once attract attention is the locomotion, which proceeds by sudden leaps, as if this ciliate were on springs.

Peritrichs (Fig. 42) are commonly bell- or vase-shaped and attached to some object by a stalk. They have a mouth zone of semimembranes (cilia fused at their base but free at their tips), which beat counterclockwise and drive food down the gullet. The body ciliation is sparse or absent. *Vorticella* is best known and has the unique honor of being the first protozoan ever seen by man. It was discovered in 1675 by the great Dutch amateur microscopist, Antonj van Leeuwenhoek, who sent a recognizable description of this genus to the Royal Society of London in one of his celebrated letters. He described how the stalk contracts, coiling like a wire spring and pulling the animal away from danger. If not further disturbed the vorticellas will slowly uncoil, straighten out, and resume feeding. Numbers are found together—they are thus *social* animals. By contrast, *Epistylis* is a *colonial* peritrich. The stalk branches, bearing an individual at the end of each branch.

The *Suctorea* differ from all other ciliates in that the cilia are present only in early stages of the life cycle and are lost when the animal becomes adult. Instead there are sucking tentacles, which are attached to the bodies of ciliate victims and serve to hold them fast in spite of their struggles. The tentacles are hollow, and through them the cell substance of the prey flows, making food vacuoles at the base of the tentacle, within the suctorean's own protoplasm. All members of this group are attached, and most of them are stalked, though the stalk is not contractile. *Podophyra* (Fig. 42) is very common in fresh water; you may be able to watch them devour paramecia or other cells in this unique fashion.

Like the free-living species, the ciliates also can provide the beginning student with excellent and readily available material for an introduction to parasitology. We shall call upon that much-used animal, the frog, without which the teaching of many phases of biology would be impossible. During your collecting trips, bring in a few frogs (any kind will do) and in your laboratory kill one by placing it in a small, tightly covered jar—a pint fruit jar is excellent—together with a piece of cotton saturated with ether or chloroform (*caution:* ether is explosive; keep away from flames). With scissors or scalpel cut through the skin and body wall of the belly by making a lengthwise cut in the middle line, and expose the internal organs. Locate the stomach and small intestine. If the frog is a female, one might confuse the coiled oviducts with the intestine; they lie on either side and convey eggs to the exterior. The intestine is also coiled but is single and more central in position and will be found to continue backward from the stomach.

Follow the small intestine to the rear until you come to the place where it abruptly enlarges to form the large intestine, or rectum. If you look closely you will observe that the enlarging occurs on one side only. That part which forms a slight bulge at one side is the cecum (blind pouch), the most important part for investigation of its protozoan contents. Cut it off while holding it with forceps, and transfer it immediately to a watch glass of warmed (about 80°F.) saline solution (formula, page 165). Cut up this piece of tissue and mash it so as to make a cloudy, milky mixture, then transfer one large drop to a clean slide, add a cover glass, and examine under low power. If the frog was infected, and most of them are, you should see one or more kinds of ciliates (Fig. 43) swimming around in this environment of salt solution, feces, and torn tissues.

Opalina is the most abundant type present. It is a large, oval, flat ciliate with cilia all over the body and a surface marking of spiral lines. *Nyctotherus* is a medium-sized heterotrich, oval and flattened. A groove starts at the front end and runs down one side to the middle, where the mouth occurs; the gullet then passes inward on a long curve, lined by an undulating membrane. This organism is easy to study under high power because of its slow movement. *Balantidium* is another heterotrich, oval and with terminal mouth apparatus. A species, *B. coli*, has the distinction of being the only ciliate parasite of man.

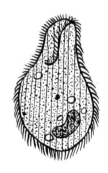

Fig. 43. *Parasitic ciliates.*
From top: Opalina;
Nyctotherus; Balantidium.

Hall, R. P., *Protozoology,* Prentice-Hall, Inc., Englewood Cliffs, N.J., 1953. Modern, general text.

Hegner, R. W., *Big Fleas Have Little Fleas, or Who's Who among the Protozoa,* The Williams & Wilkins Company, Baltimore, 1938. A fine reference on the parasitic species.

Jahn, T. L., and F. F. Jahn, *How to Know the Protozoa,* William C. Brown Company, Dubuque, Iowa, 1949. Best manual for identification; fully illustrated.

Kudo, R. R., *Protozoology,* 4th ed., Charles C Thomas, Publisher, Springfield, Ill., 1954. Standard manual on protozoa; needed by all advanced workers.

Wichterman, R., *The Biology of Paramecium,* The Blakiston Division, McGraw-Hill Book Company, Inc., New York, 1952. Full treatment for those interested in this much-studied form.

chapter seven

Simple algae and infusions

The lowest group in the plant kingdom is comprised of the Algae and Fungi. The body of this kind of plant is unlike that of such higher forms as ferns and pines in that it has no division into root, stem, and leaf; instead there is only a *thallus*. This may be a simple and more or less uniformly constructed object, ribbonlike and flat, or in the form of a thread (filamentous), or broad and leaflike. At times it may even resemble the body of a higher plant, with structures deceptively similar to root, stem, and leaf, but under the microscope no differentiation can be seen and the various tissues that characterize the mosses, ferns, and seed plants are not present.

The algae, found in blue-greens, greens, browns, and reds, run the gamut in size and form from single-celled creatures that move about like protozoa, through long filamentous species, to the many kinds of seaweeds, up to the giant kelp, which may attain 700 ft. in length, thus having a claim to fame as the longest organism on earth. We would need a telescope to study this species, rather than a microscope!

Some of your specimens will be unicellular, others multicellular strings of cells, or colonies of one shape or another; some motile, others stationary; some free, some attached. A good form to start with is *Euglena* (Fig. 44), which the botanists say is a green alga and which zoologists claim as a

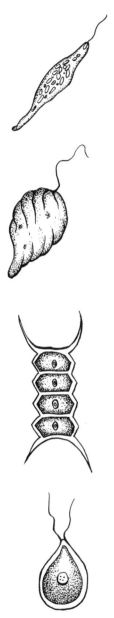

Fig. 44. *Algae.* From top: Euglena; Phacus; Scenedesmus; Chlamydomonas.

flagellate protozoan. It is small and spindle-shaped, swims rapidly through the water, and is generally present in large numbers. Its bright green color often makes whole ponds or ditches appear of this hue. There is a single flagellum, difficult to see. In very dim light and under high power the whipping of the flagellum will become evident as flashes of light. At times euglena stops swimming and turns and coils about on itself, changing shape meanwhile, a series of acts termed euglenoid movements. At or near the base of the flagellum is a bright red eyespot, sensitive to light. In a culture or aquarium the euglenas move toward the light and congregate on the illuminated side of the vessel, for to them light is life.

The green algae exhibit in simplest fashion that wonderful substance, *chlorophyll.* The word, which means "green leaf," was taken up in recent years by the makers of tooth pastes and chewing gum, who stress its deodorant properties. It is a complex pigment usually contained within small bodies, the *chloroplasts,* located in the cell substance of all green plants—in the whole plant, in the case of the unicellular algae; in the leaves and young, green stems of higher plants. It absorbs light from the sun and thus obtains the energy necessary for the chemical transformations that manufacture sugar, the basic food. In general, animals do not possess chlorophyll and cannot make their own food, while most plants other than the fungi are provided with this vital substance and can put water and carbon dioxide together to construct first sugar and then starch. So the botanists have a good argument in claiming euglena as a plant.

Phacus (Fig. 44) is top-shaped, more or less unsymmetrical, and flattened; most species have a taillike process. *Scenedesmus* (Fig. 44) is very common and easily recognized. It is a colonial type, different species of which have four, eight, or sixteen cells, arranged in one or two parallel or zigzag rows. The individual cells are oval or pointed, and the surrounding membrane may be smooth or provided with horns. *Chlamydomonas* (Fig. 44) is a small, spherical, actively swimming form, with one large and bright green chloroplast that fills the cell, and with an eyespot and two flagellums. *Volvox* (Fig. 45) is an immense (as sizes go in the microcosm) spherical colony, composed of many cells, each of which is like an

90

individual chlamydomonas. They are common in ponds and, should you chance upon them will reward you with a beautiful sight—green globes that roll swiftly along, propelled by the combined action of many flagellums.

With *Spirogyra* (Fig. 45) we pass from a spherical to a chainlike colony, the individuals forming a long strand. The chloroplast of each cell has the odd form of a spiral ribbon, running around the cylindrical cell near its outer border, and causing the whole chain to appear bright green. Spirogyra is called pond scum or water silk and is exceedingly abundant. You are certain to collect it if you secure some of the fine, slimy, green threads that form an oozy mass on the surfaces of ponds, rocks, and sticks in water or on the wet banks of streams.

Closterium (Fig. 45) is a unicellular type representing the *Desmids*, the cells of which consist of two perfectly symmetrical halves. It is crescent-shaped, and a large vacuole in each tapered end contains moving granules; look for these under high power.

Navicula (Fig. 45) is chosen as a single example of the vast assemblage of *Diatoms*, the pride and joy of a great many amateur microscopists, especially in Britain. Diatoms are unicellular plants, housed in glass boxes—shells of silica. The box is composed of two halves, termed *valves,* fitting together like a pillbox with its overlapping cover and capable of separation. This is one group with which the collecting instincts of the amateur may run riot, for there are so many species— marine, brackish, and fresh-water—living and fossil. Some collectors of diatom valves mounted on slides go in for species, others for localities, still others make gorgeous symmetrical patterns of arranged diatom valves (Fig. 81, Chapter 11). The favorite tool for handling these minute shells is a tiger's whisker mounted in a wooden handle.

Diatoms create interest in many ways:

1. They are all beautiful examples of symmetry and intricate detail at the microscopic level; many are colored and look like jewels because of the various ways in which they transmit, absorb, refract, or diffract the several components of white light. Some are pigmented.

2. The valves have slits and pores so extremely fine and

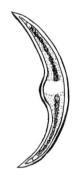

Fig. 45. *Algae.* From top: Volvox; Spirogyra; Closterium; Navicula.

closely spaced that they have become classical objects for testing the resolving power of microscope objectives. A poor lens or low power will show only the valve; higher magnification with the proper attention to resolution will disclose a series of fine lines; but the finest objectives and high N.A. will reveal that the fine lines are actually a series of pores of an extraordinary degree of minuteness.

3. Diatoms are the basis of much of the world's food. They lie at the bottom of one kind of "food pyramid," in each successive level of which the organisms get a bit larger and a bit less numerous. Thus, diatoms are eaten by protozoa, small worms, mollusks, fishes; these in turn by larger fishes; and these by heron, mink, and man, to name only a few. One biologist remarked that "all fish are diatoms," meaning that fish flesh comes originally from a diatomaceous source. The diatoms, being green algae, manufacture their organic bodies out of inorganic materials, making proteins, fats, and carbohydrates available to animals that are incapable of this manufacturing process. Interestingly enough, the largest organism ever to have evolved on this planet, the blue whale, or sulfurbottom, which can exceed 85 ft. in length and 2 million lb. in weight, lives chiefly on the diatoms found as the major component of plankton soup.

4. Diatoms have considerable economic value. Because of their siliceous composition, the fossil shells have wonderful insulating properties. Diatomaceous earth, or kieselguhr, scours our teeth (it is the chief ingredient of tooth pastes); cleans our silver and other metals, such as the chrome on automobiles; filters petroleum and sugar in their manufacturing processes; insulates refrigerator pipes; and absorbs nitroglycerin in the making of dynamite, forming an inert base to render this explosive less liable to detonate accidentally.

Altogether, diatoms are tiny but of an importance out of all proportion to their size.

The hay-infusion microcosm

In Chapter 5 the setup of this experiment was described. If you mount a drop or two of water from different regions—bottom, middle, top—of this infusion jar when it is freshly made you will probably find few if any signs of life. Apparently nothing is in the infusion except what is evident to the eye—hay and water.

But wait two or three days and try again. Within limits, the higher the temperature where the jar is standing, the more rapid the development of the microcosm. The results will now astonish you. And after a few days more there will be still greater cause for wonder. You will see organisms by the myriad: bacteria, minute flagellates, larger ones, ciliates in quite an array, and finally more complex, multicellular animals, the rotifers, and probably some worms!

Where do they all come from? Well—to begin with, if you used tap water, probably some bacteria and possibly a few algae and protozoa were introduced from that source. But by far the greater number come in on the hay, each organism in a state of suspended animation known as *encystment*, or in the form of spores or zygotes (fertilized eggs). Many protozoa, for example, have the power, when conditions of their environment become unfavorable (e.g., when the water in which they dwell dries up), to produce a thick, impervious envelope about themselves, the *cyst wall*. To do this, they round up, eject all food and crystals, lose certain of their structures, and become mere protoplasmic masses without any cell activities at all. As a *cyst* they may live for months or even years and be blown about by the wind as a component of the dust, carried from place to place.

We have already met with similar states in other situations. The life of a parasite necessitates some such arrangement when the organism passes into the host's intestine or is shed to the outer world; *Endamoeba histolytica* has a cyst stage. The zygote of spirogyra, an overwintering phase, is comparable. Bacteria produce resistant spores which spread the species widely.

With the return of favorable conditions, or if the object is blown to suitable localities where moisture is again available, the cell *excysts*—the cyst wall ruptures, the cell takes on those structures that it lost when it encysted, and it is in business again. Some species, such as euglena, reproduce by fission while encysted, so that more individuals emerge from this long sleep than entered it.

Thus is the great array of life in the microcosm accounted for as it begins its expansion. All these lower organisms reproduce very rapidly, so that from a few cysts there are shortly millions of descendants.

First to appear are the *bacteria*. Those concerned with decay may have been present on the hay, or they may have reached the infusion from the atmosphere, before the jar was covered. They attack all lifeless plants and animals and bring about decomposition. Perhaps you have never given the matter a thought, but the dead body of a horse, for example, could lie on the pasture forever, with no changes taking place, were it not for the many kinds of plants and animals that feed upon such banquets. Foremost among such plants are these same bacteria. They are exceedingly minute and unicellular and will be somewhat difficult to observe unless you have access to a high-powered microscope and adequate lighting facilities. Cut down the light and focus on the edge of decaying bits of vegetable debris.

The results of bacterial action are readily detected, however, in the form of a surface scum, a general cloudiness of the mixture, and a characteristically foul odor. The decomposition of the hay has begun. The energy stored up in the wisps of hay is being utilized by the bacteria for their life processes, and they give off in turn much simpler compounds. If uninterrupted, this procedure would continue for a long time until all the energy locked up in the hay had been dissipated or converted, whereupon the bacteria would perish from starvation.

But an enemy army now invades the scene! The protozoa have come along more slowly, but they gradually enter the picture in ever greater numbers and soon dominate the situation. First come battalions of exceedingly minute flagellates, so small that no one except the expert attempts to classify them. For the sake of convenience we shall call them all *monads* (Latin, a unit; Greek, alone). Some of them feed upon the broken-down elements of the hay that the bacteria have made available; others devour the bacteria themselves. As conditions, from their point of view, improve, the monads multiply rapidly. You may recognize them as *very* small cells that swim actively, after the fashion of euglena.

Then come the hordes of ciliates which feed upon the bacteria and monads and also on the larger flagellates. Colpidium and colpoda will doubtless be present in immense numbers. Paramecium will thrive in this mixture if a pipetteful is introduced from some pond source; it does not occur spontaneously. Larger ciliates eat the smaller ones, and so it goes —all the forms present are destructive agents. Gradually but inevitably the microcosm must run down, as all the original stored energy is exhausted through the activities of this population.

Worms and rotifers will probably show up in large numbers toward the late stages of our drama. What is needed now are some energy producers and conservers, to offset all this destruction. It may chance that certain microscopic green plants are present; if not, you may act as the God of the Machine, introducing any of several algae collected elsewhere. Then will these additions bottle up the energy in sunlight, manufacturing fresh food to restore the jaded culture. If the right proportion is at length attained, you may convert the hay-infusion microcosm into a balanced aquarium.

Putting dry hay in water started something! When you performed this simple act you initiated an entire microscopic universe, and in the space of a few days you have peered through the magic tube at the rise and fall of dynasties and have seen a world of bustling activities gradually run down until, were it not for chlorophyll, the catastrophe of wholesale starvation and death would have overtaken all.

The lettuce infusion will exhibit a parallel development, with different species, and if you find this sort of study interesting, you may try almost any form of vegetation in initiating a microcosm.

References on aquatic microscopy

Boyer, C. S., Synopsis of the North American Diatomaceae, *Proc. Nat. Acad. Sci. Phila.,* vols. 78, 79, and supplements, 1927. Comprehensive treatment; may be consulted in larger libraries.

Garnett, W. J., *Freshwater Microscopy,* Constable & Co., Ltd., London, 1953. Very fine book on collecting, mounting, studying small fresh-water specimens of plants and animals.

Needham, J. G., and P. R. Needham, *A Guide to the Study of Fresh-Water Biology,* Comstock Publishing Associates, Inc., Ithaca, N.Y., 1935. Small booklet, profusely illustrated, excellent for identification of microscopic aquatic organisms.

Prescott, G. W., *How to Know the Fresh-Water Algae,* William C. Brown Company, Dubuque, Iowa, 1954. Best manual for identification, fully illustrated.

Smith, G. M., *The Fresh-Water Algae of the United States,* 2d ed., McGraw-Hill Book Company, Inc., New York, 1950. Outstanding text in this field.

Tiffany, L. H., *Algae, the Grass of Many Waters,* Charles C Thomas, Publisher, Springfield, Ill., 1938. For all interested in the algae.

Ward, H. B., and G. C. Whipple, *Fresh-water Biology,* John Wiley & Sons, Inc., New York, 1918. A book past its fortieth birthday but still far and away the finest work on this subject in English.

See also references at end of Chapter 6.

chapter eight

Warp and woof

With this adventure into the land of textiles we shall part company for a while with living organisms and explore an industrial field. At the same time we shall begin to make some permanent microscope slide mounts and acquire experience in the simpler phases of microtechnique. After this apprenticeship we can later return to the animal and plant kingdoms and prepare organisms and their parts for study under the lens.

Our field trip this time will have to be made to the yardgoods, fabrics, and notions counters of department and dime stores, and especially to the stores of household remnants in closet, drawer, or attic. What we want will be pieces about the size of a postage stamp of as many different kinds of textiles as our interest dictates, such as wool, linen, cotton, silk, and several varieties of synthetic fabrics; yarns, string, and threads, and, in a closely allied field, examples of many kinds of paper —tissue, newsprint, linen, kraft.

Let us make a representative mount first, then describe how it is to be studied and what is to be learned from such a slide.

A fabric mount

Suppose that an old cotton dress is the first victim to be sacrificed in forming the nucleus of our slide collection. Cut a piece ½ in. square and, with a pair of fine needles, tease five or six threads away from one side, one at a time; *tease* as here used means to disentangle or separate. This will expose a number of the *threads* of which the *fabric* is made. They are either *warps*, which run lengthwise of the weaving loom, or *woofs,* also called *wefts,* that run crosswise. The shuttle that goes back and forth horizontally carries the woof. Now snip off two or three of these projecting threads from either side of a central one that is left standing; this will make room to fray out this one thread so as to expose the separate *yarns* which, by twisting, make the thread; and, further, to fray some of these at their ends and so expose the ultimate structure, the cotton *fiber.* When mounted, this piece of goods will show fabric, weave, thread, yarn, and fiber, all in one. TEASING NEEDLES may be bought or homemade. There are bone-handled needle holders, equipped with chucks, to hold any size of sewing needle, which can be changed as needed. A satisfactory handle is made from a large match stick, the so-called kitchen match, by cutting off the head with a razor blade, inserting a needle into the cut end, lengthwise, slowly and carefully for ¼ in. or so. If you split the match stick, take another one and try again. Twist the needle and remove it, then replace it eye end first along with an adhesive, such as Duco Household Cement. Allow cement to harden. Tape the handle if you prefer. Another suggestion: turn down one end of a 6-in. length of ¼-inch dowel in a pencil sharpener, and mount a needle in this tapered end.

The final work on the fabric mount is best done on a clean, blank slide, and then xylene is added.

XYLENE (zī′–lĕn; Greek, wood) is a hydrocarbon occurring in coal and wood tars and certain petroleums. It finds important uses in microscopy as a *clearer* (clearing agent), rendering substances translucent and paving the way for mounting. In English one says xylene, toluene, and benzene, but in German usage xylol, toluol, and benzol are favored. Thus xylene and xylol are the same thing. It evaporates rapidly, so keep the xylene bottle closed at all times when not actually pouring from it.

CANADA BALSAM is a natural resin, a turpentine obtained from the balsam fir, and until recently was universally preferred as a *mountant* for the majority of slide preparations. It is prepared as a solid, then dissolved in xylene for use in microscopy —it should be thinned to the right consistency. The receptacle of choice is a *balsam bottle*, with loosely fitting glass lid and applicator rod. Keep it in the dark when not in use; exposure to light gradually darkens the balsam. Put a small piece of marble in the bottle; this keeps the balsam neutral; otherwise it tends to become slightly acid, a change harmful to stains. Thin with xylene from time to time as needed and, to exclude dust and water vapor, keep covered at all times except at the instant of use. Some subjects require a thicker balsam than others, and accordingly some workers maintain two bottles, containing thick and thin balsams, but for the average mount the balsam is right when it will flow slowly as a sticky rope from the applicator rod when this is lifted, and at the end will deliver two or three separate drops. It is important to raise and replace the rod smoothly, with as little disturbance of the balsam as possible, thus avoiding stirring and whipping, which incorporate a great many air bubbles. Such bubbles are troublesome and do not work out readily.

PERMOUNT is a trade name (Fisher Scientific Company) for one of the several new synthetic mountants now preferred by most technicians. Such a preparation can be made chemically pure, permanently water-white, and neutral. It is thinned with toluene.

CENTERING GUIDE Use a white card, such as a 3 by 5 index card. Place a slide in the center of this card, and draw around it to form its outline. Remove the slide and with a ruler draw the diagonals. Replace the slide. The point where the diagonals cross (seen through the glass) marks the center of the slide; keep this card to use whenever, for the sake of neatness or uniformity, it is desirable to center your subjects.

MOUNTING With a clean slide on the centering guide, the prepared fabric centered on the slide, xylene and mountant at hand, and a clean cover glass in position to grasp, use a pipette to place 2 drops (more for thicker fabrics) of xylene on the goods. Allow to soak for two or three minutes—the exact time doesn't matter in this case, but do not allow the specimen to become dry. If the cloth starts turning opaque, add more xylene. After the clearer has been thoroughly absorbed, add one large or two small drops of balsam (or other mountant) and immediately apply the cover glass, using the method employed in Chapter 5. As the cover falls into place, the mountant should spread out evenly beneath, rather promptly. If it does not, it is too thick. The principal trick to learn is to add a quantity of mountant that will fill all the area under the cover yet will not run out upon the uncovered portions of the slide. As you try different thicknesses of papers and fabrics, you will find that a very thin mount requires only 1 drop, a thicker one needs 2. Fabrics are easy, and by the time several of these slides have been made, you will readily complete more difficult subjects with scarcely a thought and certainly without making any of the sticky messes that are likely to greet your first attempts.

In cleaning up glassware, microscope, table, or hands inadvertently soiled with a mountant, use the solvent for the particular resin, or a similar chemical; in this case, for either balsam or Permount, use xylene. To remove xylene, use waste alcohol.

Flaming the cover glass. Moisture is fatal to permanent mounts in a resin, and neither xylene nor balsam will tolerate the slightest trace of water. To demonstrate: place 1 drop of xylene and 1 drop of water together on a slide, and observe the milky, opaque result.

To ensure absence of water, many workers prefer to *flame* each cover glass before using it. A low, relatively cool flame is needed, and the *alcohol lamp* is the preferred type. A laboratory Bunsen burner, however, can be used if turned moderately low. Holding the cover in a forceps, pass it forward and back through the flame with moderate speed, then apply it to the mount. After you have cracked one or two covers you will learn the proper speed for this act.

Aftertreatment of slides

DRYING Before a freshly made slide can be used to any extent beyond mere examination, it should be dried. Balsam turns to a solid by evaporation of the xylene solvent, requiring about two weeks on the average. The synthetic resins dry much more rapidly. In most cases, however, a *slide dryer* is in order, and for this purpose biological laboratories use low-temperature ovens or incubators (Fig. 86, Chapter 12). If you plan much work in this field you should own some form of incubator; a secondhand stove-top oven is readily adaptable. For drying slides, only moderate temperatures, such as that from a single 40-watt bulb, should be used; *dry* your slides, don't fry them! If an attempt is made to dry slides in a tilted or vertical position, the mountant will be likely to flow off the slide. Do *not* dry slides by exposing them to direct sunlight; this will injure most kinds of slides, fading stained preparations and darkening balsam mounts.

CORRECTING ERRORS OR DEFICIENCIES   If the cover glass is on crooked, it may be straightened by slowly moving it with a needle, applied as a poker to one edge, before the mountant hardens. If the material needs straightening, it will be possible in many cases to straighten it with needles. Moisten a needle with xylene and run it under the cover, slowly and carefully, poke the material into position, and remove the needle, twisting it as it is withdrawn. When desirable to remove the cover, stand the slide vertically in a jar of xylene (see description of the Coplin jar under Staining, Chapter 12) and let the cover fall off by itself, reclaim the material, and remount it, using fresh glassware.

If there is too much mountant on a slide, remove as much as possible while it is still fluid by wrapping a thin cloth around the tips of forceps, a pencil, orange stick, or other blunt device, dipping the cloth in xylene, and wiping, using care not to touch the cover glass. After the mountant is dry and hard, it may be scraped away with a knife or safety-razor blade held vertically to the slide; it will flake off readily. Finish with a cloth *dampened* in xylene (not *wet*). This can even be done to the top of the coverglass, if one develops a delicate touch, but always keep metal away from the cover's edge; one slight nick and the glass will shatter.

If there is not enough mountant on a slide, there will be air holes under the cover glass. If the empty space is large enough to be unsightly or bothersome and does not communicate with the exterior, force a way into it with a warmed needle—not hot enough to crack the cover! When or if the air hole is exposed to the outside, add more mountant in the same way that you supplied more culture to a mount of living protozoa, by letting the new fluid run in under the cover by capillarity. Add a little at a time until the space is filled. Avoid getting any mountant on top of the cover.

Air bubbles under cover will probably work out by themselves and are best ignored. If they persist, soak off the cover and remount.

CLEANING   Mostly, cleaning will be concerned with getting rid of excess mountant, a process already discussed. But there may be other substances to remove, notably stains in the case of slides to be prepared later that involve the staining procedure. Clean off any excess stains with their own solvents: water, if an aqueous solution was employed, such as hematoxylin; strong alcohol, if the stain was an alcoholic solution, such as eosin. In stubborn cases, use the hydrochloric acid destain (Chapter 10). Greases should be removed with xylene, toluene, ether, or carbon tetrachloride. In all these operations, keep the reagents away from the cover glass. Polish the finished slide with any detergent; Calgonite is preferred in many laboratories, although powdered Bon Ami is still one of the best products with which to shine glassware.

LABELING   Gummed microscope slide labels are sold by all general supply houses, either as cut labels in boxes or as perforated sheets in book form. For a small additional sum, certain firms will print on the labels your name and any other data, such as name of school, institution, or city; it is advisable to have this printing done at the outset if you intend making a personal and permanent slide collection. It is best to print the title on by hand on the label before it is applied to the slide, using black India ink and a fine pen, such as a Spencerian No. 1, or a crow quill. The printing should be painstakingly done and should present a neat, balanced appearance. A good slide is worthy of a proper label. A sloppy label is indicative of sloppy technique.

Information to appear on the label varies with the preparation but in general should include the following: the *subject*

—what the material is; the *source*, if the subject is a part of a larger object; the *view* presented, or the *type* of slide. Sometimes it is important to state the fixer and stain(s) used. Examples: (1) Linen Fabric (in relatively large letters) across the top half of the label, using two lines, then a ruled underlining or divider, followed by w.m. in smaller type in the bottom half of the label, indicating *whole mount*, a type of slide in which the material is mounted entire, without sectioning. (2) Human Blood, dividing line, Wright's. It is understood that protozoa, blood, bacteria, etc., will be mounted as a *smear*, actually a whole mount of very small objects, and so this designation may be omitted from the label. Wright's is a well-known stain for blood, hence the one word is sufficient in this case. (3) Intestine, dividing line, cat, c.s., dividing line, Zenker's (left bottom corner, fine print), H&E (right bottom corner). Here the identity of the organ is the important thing, and receives major billing; whether the intestine is from cat, rat, or dog is essential information but of secondary importance; c.s. is the standard abbreviation for *cross section;* Zenker's is the fixer, and H&E denominate the stains, hematoxylin and eosin. Special stains need to be spelled out, but every microscopist will recognize the abbreviation of these two routine ones.

Nothing can beat saliva for wetting the label; lick one carefully, as you would a postage stamp, apply it exactly, then wrap the forefinger of each hand in a cloth, such as a clean handkerchief, and proceed systematically to iron out the label on the slide. Unless all parts are thoroughly pressed, with motions from center to edge and along all four edges, the label will not stick completely and permanently; it is necessary to be fussy about this and not to dismiss the task hastily or carelessly. Inspection of the back of the labeled slide will show whether or not all portions are adherent.

There are glass-writing pencils, in soft wax of various colors, for temporary labeling; there are special inks for writing on glass; there are diamond-tipped pencils and carborundum-pointed ones for scratching the glass to make permanent records on the slides; and there are blank slides with a marginal square inch ground on one face to permit writing on this surface with a pencil, but the great majority of microscopists still prefer gummed paper labels.

How may we best study a slide of a fabric whole mount? The protozoa and algae we have been observing are *transparent* objects and are seen by means of *transmitted light*—that which comes from below, via the mirror or substage lamp, and is transmitted by the object. If we place a coin, such as a silver half dollar, on the stage and cover the aperture, it is obvious that we must illuminate this subject from above. The coin is an *opaque* object, and the direct illumination is termed *incident* or *reflected light*. A piece of fabric is intermediate, being more or less *translucent*, i.e., it lets some light through but does not reveal objects beneath it. In such a case a combination of *both* forms of illumination works best.

Incident light may be provided by a student gooseneck lamp or by microscope lamps such as those shown in Figures 10, 11, 27, 58. Special gadgets exist for this purpose. The *vertical illuminator* throws a strong beam of light into the microscope tube from a horizontal source; the light is then directed downward through the tube by means of a mirror, prism, or plate and focused on the object by the objective, which acts as a condenser; then the light is reflected back up through the objective to the observer. Another style of lamp, the *Silverman illuminator,* forms a collar of lamps around the neck of the objective, with a reflector to direct all the rays downward. The do-it-yourself craftsman will be able to rig the fountain-pen type of small flashlight, battery-operated, alongside the microscope tube, or arrange a series of small flashlight bulbs in a circle around the objective collar, as a means of securing and directing concentrated incident light if his work is such as to demand a considerable amount of this form of illumination, justifying the necessary time and trouble.

Assuming, then, that some form of incident lighting is at hand, inspect the fabric slide by transmitted light, then by incident light alone, with a piece of black photomount paper over the stage aperture, and then with both kinds of illumination at once. In most cases you will find the combined lighting gives superior results.

104

When a series of these fabric mounts has been made, it is time to study them critically and comparatively, to learn some of the many facts that such slides can demonstrate.

Woven patterns

Formerly a *fabric* was anything put together, any manufactured object, such as a boat or a building; but today the word is used solely to designate textiles. Likewise the term *weave* has altered meanings. There are six textile structures, only one of which is actually woven, but commonly they are all lumped together as examples of weaving. Spinning and weaving are very ancient arts, so intimately associated with the work of woman that the spinning wheel has become her symbol in Caucasian countries, and we still speak, in law and literature, of the distaff side of the family. In Africa, on the contrary, while women may spin, i.e., form a twisted thread or yarn out of fibers, they may not weave, the loom being the prerogative of the male. If you are interested in this subject, consult the articles on spinning, weaving, looms, and textiles in encyclopedias.

The simplest design in weaving is to arrange a series of parallel longitudinal threads, the warps, then intersect these at right angles with a second set of parallel horizontal threads, the woofs, each woof passing successively and alternately under then over the series of warps. This makes *plain cloth*, or simply *plain* (Fig. 46); if made by hand, it is *homespun;* if machine-made and of cotton, it is called *factory*. But num-

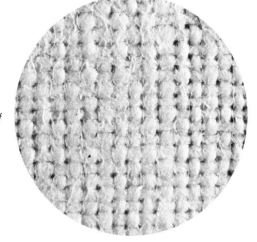

Fig. 46. Plain cloth, showing the pattern of simple weaving.

berless variations on this simple theme are possible. Alternating thick and thin warps and woofs produces a corded goods called *rep*, or *repp* (Fig. 47). Either warps or woofs may be skipped, according to some prearranged plan of weaving, as when each woof skips over two successive warps, then passes under the third, or passes over five and under two. Endless variety of this sort exists in fabrics known as *twills*, the skipping resulting in diagonal patterns (Fig. 48). By having, for example, every fifth or tenth woof differ from the remainder in composition, size, or color, many designs may be woven into the goods, the special woofs being *pattern threads*.

The other methods of fabricating goods are knitting, felting, plaiting, netting, and lacemaking. The chief product made by knitting is *hosiery fabric;* we shall want to make a mount from a piece of discarded stocking and compare the method of joining the threads with that used in woven goods. Slips, undergarments, T-shirts, and rayon-Jersey dresses are other hosiery-fabric items. *Felted fabrics* are made by an altogether different scheme; the fibers are wetted, rolled, and pressed under heat with a sizing matrix. Carpets and hats are the principal products, and animal fibers such as wool, hair, and fur are the main materials. A piece of goods that is *plaited* differs from other types in that only one series of threads is interlaced, and that is not interlaced at right angles. Of all forms of textile manipulation, this one has been performed by more people than all others combined, for most women have braided their hair, and the small boy does not live who has not plaited a boondoggle out of grass, straw, string, or rawhide. Straw hats are commonly made in this manner, as are rugs and matting. Handbag handles, dress trimmings, and braid are other examples of plaiting. In England the word for this kind of fabrication is pronounced "plat," to rhyme with "flat," and may be spelled that way, too. In the United States it has been "plait," rhyming with "plate," but is now more often heard as "pleat."

Net and lace fabrics are openwork. In *nets*, wherever threads cross they are tied by knots; fish nets, tennis nets, and hair nets are familiar examples. Not everything called a net is actually netting. A butterfly net is more likely to be open weaving or lace. Malines is a fine silk mesh used in millinery

Fig. 47. Rayon repp fabric.　　　　*Fig. 48. Cotton gabardine twill.*

and dressmaking; tulle is the more recent term (both terms come from names of French cities). These are not true nets, as the intersections are not knotted. Veils are of many patterns, as your microscope can show you, some netted, some with complex twisted and woven designs that qualify them as laces.

Different from all other fabrics is *lace*. It is also much more beautiful and intricate, as there is always a pattern involved— geometric, flowery, or pictorial. Some parts are merely twisted, or looped, or stitched; others are plaited, netted, or woven. Again, the microscope will reveal the lacemaker's design and methods.

Threads and fibers

Here is a spool of ordinary thread, marked as to denier, or weight (No. 40), as to length (160 yd.), and stated to be "best six cord," indicating the number of yarns. The composition is not given but is understood to be of cotton if not otherwise designated. Frayed and mounted for microscopic examination, the thread is seen to be twisted from six "cords," which are the yarns, and these in turn are twisted from cotton fibers. Another thread may be made of silk, rayon, or linen. How may they be distinguished?

Fibers are from many sources and should be classified first

according to the old child's game, as "animal, vegetable, or mineral." They are identified by a variety of means, including a burning test. One determines first whether or not the fiber will burn; if it does, the color of the flame, nature of the smoke and ash, odor, and whether or not the fire is self-extinguishing help to identify the fiber. Also helpful in determinations are the color on applying various special stains, observation of whether the fiber goes into solution in cuprammonium hydroxide, flotation test results, sizes, and other factors, but by far the most basic of all the tests is examination under the microscope.

Far and away the most important animal fibers are wool and silk. *Wool*, second in value only to cotton among natural textile fibers, is the underfur of sheep as improved through selective breeding to eliminate the coarser guard hairs. Like the other animal hairs used as textile fibers—chiefly *alpaca* (from llamas), *cashmere* (from Cashmere goats), and *mohair* (from Angora goats)—wool fibers are covered with cuticular scales (Fig. 103, Chapter 13), a sure indication of hair. Animal fibers are best mounted in water for identification, the refractive index being better for the purpose than that of resins.

Silk, without a qualifying adjective, is understood to be that of the domesticated silkworm, *Bombyx mori*, the culture of which was begun by the ancient Chinese. Silk is the product of a pair of salivary glands, a liquid that hardens immediately upon exposure to air. The caterpillar discharges fluid from both glands simultaneously, forming a silk thread that is composed of two filaments, side by side, each about $\frac{12}{100}$ in. in diameter and anywhere from 800 to 1,200 yd. long! Rotating its head with clocklike regularity for about three days, the larva wraps itself in the silk to make a thick cocoon, an admirable protection from all animals except man, who comes along and drops the cocoon into boiling soap solution to remove the sticky binding material. Raw silk, before treatment, is harsh to the touch, stiff in texture, and a soiled, yellowish-white in color. Boiling removes the *sericin,* or silk glue, 20 to 30 per cent of the whole, and leaves two filaments, made of *fibroin*, that are readily separated and are soft, white, and lustrous. Under magnification, raw silk exhibits a continuous double thread with adherent irregular masses, while degummed silk displays a structureless filament with no internal details at all. *Tussah silk*, from an undomesticated silkworm, shows longitudinal internal striations and is brown in color.

Of vegetable fibers, the all-important *cotton* is a seed hair that, upon the bursting of the ripened boll, collapses, twists, and forms a flattened, convoluted tube. The twisting reverses at frequent intervals, and there is about the same amount of clockwise as anticlockwise turning. Under the microscope, the cotton fiber appears flat, hollow, twisted—unique features that at once identify it. Another plant hair is *kapok*, growing mostly on the fruit pod, less on the seed of the silk cotton tree. In a water mount this fiber will appear as a thin-walled, cylindrical tube with air bubbles at frequent intervals.

Other vegetable textiles are mostly *bast fibers*, woody material in the bark of many plants, valuable for their strength. Bast consists of elongate, pointed cells with thick walls; the cells may be cemented together to make a continuous filament. Chief among such fibers are flax, jute, hemp, ramie, and the similar sisal, though the last is from a leaf rather than from a stem. It is recommended that bast fibers be mounted in liquid paraffin for identification. As paraffin will mix with xylene, one should go through this clearer first; then, for a permanent mount, either use another piece of the same material and go from xylene to mountant, as before, or if the same specimen is wanted, pass from paraffin back into xylene and then into the mountant.

Flax is a blue-flowered annual plant with long silky bast fibers in the stem. These are freed by *retting* (maceration, or rotting in water, involving bacterial action). The seeds are extremely valuable, yielding linseed oil, used in the manufacture of paints, and the residue is made into linseed meal, for feeding cattle. Flaxseed meal is the same, but with the oil left in. The seeds are used extensively in medicine. The retted stems yield a fiber that is spun into *linen* thread, thence woven into linen cloth, cambric, lawn, and other variants. Flax fibers occur in bundles, marked with prominent cross striations, often in the form of an X.

Jute is a stem bast fiber that runs in meshworks, from 5

to 10 ft. in length, in either of two East Indian plants of the linden family. Because this fiber is injured by wetting, it is used principally in the manufacture of sacking, burlap, and the cheaper sorts of twine. The fibers run in bunches and resemble a bundle of sticks under magnification, without the cross markings found in flax.

The *hemp* plant is a widely cultivated Asiatic member of the mulberry family, whose flowers and leaves yield the narcotics, bhang and hashish, and whose bast fibers are made into cloth and cordage. The fibers occur in bundles with cross markings, similar to those in flax, but the hemp bundles are coarser and the cross markings are more numerous. *Manila hemp* on the other hand comes from a banana in the Philippines and is used for native textiles, matting, canvas, and ropes and also for the familiar brown, or Manila, paper.

The fibers of *ramie*, or China grass, are the strong and silky bast fibers of a member of the nettle family, in demand for weaving into fine fabrics. The ramie canes require retting and degumming before spinning is possible. The individual fibers are large and thick-walled, with a demonstrable lumen (cavity), and have both cross and longitudinal striations.

Sisal fibers occur in bundles, are thin-walled, and have no markings, but they show unique spiral vessels here and there. Named from a Yucatán port, the term describes any of several Mexican and Central American agaves, especially the henequen, now cultivated in Florida and the West Indies for their white fibers. *Esparto* is a Spanish grass whose fibers are made into a coarse cloth, paper, cordage, shoes, and other articles.

The only contribution to textiles from the mineral kingdom until recently was *asbestos*, occurring as long, fine, silky fibers, derived from amphibole (gray asbestos) or from chrysotile, a variety of serpentine (white asbestos). They can be spun, but the practice usually is to mix them with small amounts of cotton, rayon, or other vegetable fibers in the spinning procedure. The woven fabric is well known for its fire-resistant qualities and is used in clothing, gloves, curtains, roofing, and other articles. Asbestos fibers can be subdivided repeatedly until beyond the view of anything save the electron microscope; thus, under ordinary magnification one of the identifying characteristics will be the variation in diameter of the fibers; also they show no structural features.

Metals are now being spun into yarns along with the older, regulation fibers, such as silk, cotton, or rayon. One such thread on the market is Lurex, varying in composition for different purposes and capable of being made up in widely diversified colors and patterns in fabrics designed for clothing, upholstery, and draperies. These goods are fascinating when magnified.

Glass is receiving increased attention as a textile material, and various processes for spinning and weaving Fiberglas find important outlets in clothing, awnings, and insulating materials. The fibers will appear perfectly clear and of uniform diameter throughout when magnified.

Mineral wool, or *slag wool*, resembles spun glass and is made by blowing a jet of air or steam through blast-furnace slag. It is used as an insulating packing in pipes and furnaces.

The twentieth century is the era of manufactured fibers, also termed synthetic or artificial. *Rayon*, or artificial silk, first and still the most important of these, is made by three main processes from cellulose. As with real silk, the solution is ejected through spinnerets and hardens upon exposure; it becomes cylindrical, solid, structureless, and has no ends, other than start and finish of a run, except those cut by man. Thus a single silk or rayon fiber will have two cut ends, unlike bast fibers that have two tapering, pointed, natural ends. *Viscose rayon*, from refined wood pulp treated with caustic soda and carbon bisulfide, shows longitudinal striations in the magnified fiber. *Cuprammonium rayon* is made from cotton linters (short fibers left on the seed after ginning) by treatment with copper sulfate and ammonia. The fibers are perfectly clear, without striations. *Acetate rayon* shows deep striations or grooves when magnified. These fibers are produced after acetic acid and other reagents make cellulose acetate from cotton linters.

The synthetic polymer fibers, including a rapidly increasing number all marketed under proprietary names, such as Nylon, Orlon, and Dacron, are an outgrowth of the modern chemistry of plastics. They are all cylindrical and structureless under the microscope.

After learning the characteristics of the chief textile fibers and building a slide collection of known specimens, the beginner is ready to try his hand at the identification of unknowns. There are three main ways in which textiles have been misrepresented in merchandising. First, inferior materials have been manufactured and sold for better-quality goods; examples are kempy and shoddy wools. *Kemps* are coarse, thick hairs from scrub animals; they are without cuticular scales and will not take dyes. *Shoddy* is the waste from spinning or weaving woolens, reclaimed and used over again, usually mixed with better wool or with cotton. Under the microscope, physical appearance identifies kempy wool, shortness of fiber proclaims the shoddy. Thus, a piece of goods may be 100 per cent pure wool, as advertised, and still be of poor quality.

The second fraudulent procedure is a misstatement of quantities, as in giving false information about gauge and denier—number of threads per inch, and diameter of thread (expressed by weight), respectively. Third, and most important, is the substitution of one fiber for another. Always, if misrepresentation is involved, a cheaper and inferior fiber is substituted, e.g., cotton is mixed with wool and the completed fabric is claimed to be "all wool and a yard wide."

Fortunately we are living in an era of ever-increasing honesty in merchandise labeling, some of it compelled by law and some by competition, named brands striving to establish reputations for purity and quality. The male microscopist will discover what his female counterpart already knows—that artificial fibers are not necessarily inferior to natural ones: indeed, for many purposes or in many cases they are superior, because of absolute control over purity and uniformity in the manufacturing processes. Mixed goods are now very popular and are marked as such, e.g., cotton and Nylon sheer fabric (Fig. 49) or silk and Orlon. These illustrations will demonstrate that investigations of this sort under the microscope may be very interesting.

Fig. 49. Cotton and Nylon sheer fabric. Individual threads show.

112

Paper

While not textiles, the various papers are made from the same source as the vegetable textile fibers—cellulose—and thus appropriately may be considered here. Wood pulp is the chief raw material, with esparto grass and rags running second. The source substance is reduced to a pulp, which is then dried on a flat sieve and pressed so that the fine fibers are felted into a continuous thin sheet. In making a slide, simply cut a ½-in. square of the paper sample, center it on a slide, and apply xylene and then the mountant. Examine all but very thick papers by transmitted light only, and look for individual fibers. Paper from wood pulp will display fibers that show pits and spirals, indicating that these were once living cells in the wood of trees, for the conduction of water. Nonwoody sources for paper will have no such appearance.

Suggested papers for mounting include cigarette (rice-straw) paper, lens and tissue papers, facial and toilet tissues, toweling, newsprint, bond, linen (fine stationery), calendered and supercalendered papers from the "slick" magazines, and kraft, or brown, paper.

In addition, include in your mounts certain items that will illustrate the methods of reproduction of illustrations.

Engraving methods

There are numerous procedures that can be used in reproducing illustrative material in the printing process. Chief among them are wood engraving, line engraving on zinc, copper, or stereotype-metal blocks, etching, dry point, stipple, mezzotint, aquatint, lithographing or the more recent photoengraving, photolithographing, photogravure, and rotogravure. In *wood engraving*, the oldest form, the design to be reproduced is left at the original level of the wooden block while the surrounding areas are cut away; thus it is called a *relief* method. When the block is inked, only the raised portions print. A *zinc plate*, commonly called a cut or a block, has replaced the wooden block for reproduction of simple line drawings. When the reproduction is magnified, no screen appears; the work looks the same as without enlargement, only coarser. Use black and white comic-strip pictures or line drawings from magazine illustrations as examples. The relief printing of type and blocks is termed *letterpress* (Fig. 50).

Line engravings are cut into metal, the grooves are filled with ink, and it is these depressions that print; the method is *intaglio*, which in Italian means exactly the same as the English *engraving* (Fig. 53). Chemicals are employed to "bite" the metal and remove it in *etching*. A metal plate of zinc (coarse), copper (fine), or steel (finest) is coated with a *resist*, or *ground*, of various waxes or resins. The ground is scratched away with the etching needle to reproduce the

Fig. 50. Enlarged view of detail from comic strip, an example of letterpress. Continuous lines; no halftone screen.

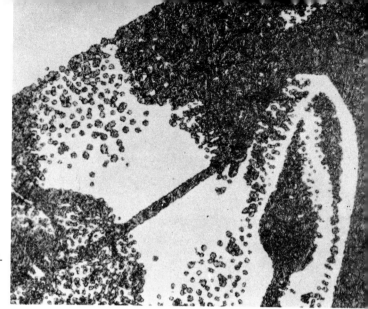

Fig. 51. Portion of man's head, an example of a half-tone engraving. Detail made up of dots, showing use of a screen.

design, then the metal is eaten where it is not protected. Line work of high quality is done by either engraving or etching; a search through old copies of printed reproductions should yield samples.

Very different is the photographic process in any of its many forms. *Halftone screens* are mechanically ruled engravings on plate glass, the gratings filled with black. For coarse newsprint, screens are 60 line (60 lines per inch); for magazine black and white, 120 to 150; and for color work, 150 to 200. When a photograph is rephotographed upon a sensitized copper plate through such a screen, the subject is broken up into a series of dots, which are then etched to form a relief engraving (Fig. 51). A 60-line newspaper halftone will contain 3,600 dots to the square inch, of various shades of light and dark. Seen with the naked eye, these dots run together to reproduce the photograph, but we have noted earlier that this screen can be resolved by viewing it through the pinhole card. Slightly higher magnification may be needed to detect finer screens, though a hand lens usually suffices, while with 100× all semblance to the original is lost. When portions of illustrations from newspapers, ordinary magazines, and supercalendered work are made as microslide whole mounts, comparison of fineness of screen is facilitated.

Likewise the methods of reproducing colored illustrations will be found to be fascinating. The face of the pretty girl in the slick magazine advertisement becomes just a meaningless jumble of colored dots. If you will read in encyclopedias about the three-color process, then make a few slides, the subject will repay your time.

As a final item, we shall steal a bit of the subject matter from our closing chapter, on scientific crime detection, to discuss some interesting documents printed by the government. Mount a postage stamp as a permanent slide preparation and examine it, noting the absence of a screen. This is a letterpress specimen.

The most intricate type of all reproductions and the finest example of the engraver's art can be inspected under the microscope by the simple procedure of placing a crisp new $1 bill beneath the spring clips of your instrument's stage, with the bill as flat as possible, moving it so as to scan one portion after another, and both sides. Use both transmitted and incident illumination, alternately.

The Bureau of Engraving and Printing in Washington, D.C., that manufactures our paper money, employs the world's most skilled engravers and takes elaborate precautions against counterfeiting. First, the *bank-note paper* has a characteristic feel, crispness, and crackle when snapped or handled that is exceedingly difficult to imitate, and of course the details of manufacture of this paper are closely guarded secrets. Since 1885 red and blue silk fibers have been incorporated in United States currency paper, and the making of this sort of paper for other purposes is prohibited by law. A counterfeiter can only imitate this feature by using colored inks, a fraud readily apparent under magnification. On the face, or obverse, of the bill (Fig. 52), the phrase at the top center, "silver certificate," identifies the class of money. The *treasury seal* (obverse, to right of portrait) and *serial number* (obverse, upper right and lower left) are printed in blue in this class. Other issues are United States notes (red seal and numbers) and Federal Reserve notes (green).

Above the portrait (Fig. 53), the words "The United States of America" form an example of *black line work* (black on white), whereas the "one dollar" below the portrait is *white*

Fig. 52. Right: *Obverse of United States banknote, locating chief features.*
Fig. 53. Below: *Portrait of Washington on one-dollar bill, genuine and counterfeit. (Both by special permission of the Chief, United States Secret Service, Treasury Department. Further reproduction in whole or in part is strictly prohibited.)*

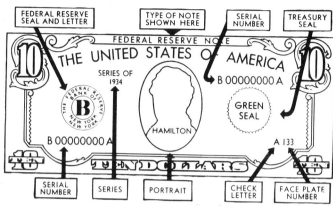

FEDERAL RESERVE SEAL AND LETTER

TYPE OF NOTE SHOWN HERE

SERIAL NUMBER

TREASURY SEAL

FEDERAL RESERVE NOTE

THE UNITED STATES OF AMERICA

SERIES OF 1934

B 00000000 A

THE FEDERAL RESERVE BANK OF NEW YORK NEW YORK

B

GREEN SEAL

HAMILTON

B 00000000 A

A 133

TEN DOLLARS

SERIAL NUMBER

SERIES

PORTRAIT

CHECK LETTER

FACE PLATE NUMBER

SILVER CERTIFICATE
FIES THAT THERE IS ON DEPOSIT IN THE TRE
NED STATES OF A

WASHINGTON

ONE DOLLAR
ER PAYABLE TO THE BEARER ON D

line work (white on black), with the spaces surrounding the letters, instead of the letters themselves, carrying the ink, a very difficult form of intaglio engraving and one that is hard to imitate. The background of the portrait, the shading of the large numeral "1" to the left of this portrait, of the "one" occupying the center of the back (reverse) of the bill, the "one dollar" below this, and the background of the obverse of the great seal of the United States, together with the shield covering the eagle, are made by a *parallel-ruling machine*, a costly device that rules the lines with mathematical exactitude, impossible to duplicate freehand. Even more elaborate are the *lacework scrolls* on the obverse and *fish-net scrolls* on the reverse borders. Examine them closely and note the precision of these intricate designs. They are done by means of a *rose engine*, also called a cycloidal engine or geometrical lathe, invented by Asa Spencer around 1818. The work is called *engine turning* or *geometrical-lathe work*. This wonderful machine, with its numberless eccentric movements, can reproduce continuous patterns of any conceivable design. Observe that not one of these fine lines is broken or joins another; each is endless and absolutely regular, with no defect in uniformity of curve, width, or degree of shading. One of these lathes costs a small fortune, and it is obvious that a man wealthy enough to own a rose engine, along with a parallel-ruling machine, to say nothing of his own paper mill, is not likely also to be an expert engraver who would turn to counterfeiting as a career!

Always in black is the small *check letter*, seen at the right of the large upper left-corner numeral on the obverse; it appears again near the lower right corner in conjunction with the *face plate number*, which identifies the steel plate from which the bill was printed. There will be also a *series* designation, such as "Series 1935 E," and the facsimile *signatures* of the treasurer of the United States and of the secretary of the treasury. The words "Washington, D.C." constitute an *overprint*, superposed upon the treasury seal. The *portrait* on the obverse and the two faces of the *great seal* on the reverse occupy *windows*. No one man does all this work; specialists take over at different stages, one man, for example, doing only portraits.

After minutely inspecting a clean new bill, examine an old one and observe what abrasion and creasing do to the work; the average life of a dollar bill is only eight months! A constant flow of old bills streams from the banks of the nation back to the Bureau of Engraving and Printing to be destroyed and replaced by a flow of new bills in the opposite direction.

References

Calkin, J. B., *Microscopy of Paper,* TAPPI (Technical Association of Pulp and Paper Industry), N.Y.; 1937. Fine guide, bibliography.

Matthews, J. M., and H. T. Mauersberger, *Textile Fibers; Their Physical, Microscopical, and Chemical Properties,* 5th ed., John Wiley & Sons, Inc., New York, 1947. Comprehensive text and reference.

Schwarz, E. R., *Textiles and the Microscope,* McGraw-Hill Book Company, Inc., New York, 1934. Complete, concise manual covering all phases; a standard reference.

The Textile Institute, *Identification of Textile Materials,* Manchester, England, 1951. Illustrated atlas and guide.

United States Secret Service, Treasury Dept., *Know Your Money.* Obtainable from the Superintendent of Documents, U.S. Government Printing Office, Washington 25, D.C., 15 cents.

chapter nine

This crumbling world

Journeying outdoors once more, we shall take a look at the crust of this old planet on which we live. The geologist, chemist, and physicist are all interested in what the microscope has to say about terra firma, and we too may spend many a profitable session on this subject.

Geology

Sand is a good material with which to begin. All we shall need by way of collecting equipment is an outfit of *shell vials* with Bakelite screw caps, or pillboxes, labels for the vials, and our knapsack. Specimens may be collected from a wide variety of places, from a small pocket of sand along the creek margin, from larger deposits on the riverbank or sand bar, the ocean beach, the desert, the dune—sand is literally everywhere. It is composed mainly of *quartz crystals*, the naturally occurring form of silica (silicon dioxide), from which glass is made, and silicon is second only to oxygen in abundance in the earth's crust. Silicates form by far the largest class of minerals.

Here is a vial of sand collected from a creek bed in the northern United States. We pour the contents into a flat container; in the laboratory it would be half a *Petri dish*, in the home a kitchen utensil, perhaps a pie tin. Warm in an oven or slide dryer at low temperature, shaking the container occasionally to turn the grains over, until they are thoroughly dry. Place 2 drops of mountant on a slide, gather some of the sand on the tip of a knife blade or a spatula, and, holding the blade over the mountant and close to it, tap it with any metal object, such as a table knife, so that the sand grains are jarred into the resin and distributed more or less evenly throughout; then add a cover glass. No xylene is used. Do not add too much sand; the grains should be scattered so that individuals may be seen; avoid piles or masses of sand, as such clumps are not suitable for observation.

Under magnification the quartz grains will appear colorless or very pale brown; they will be angular, some with fairly sharp edges or points, depending on how long a time has elapsed since they were eroded or weathered out of their parent granitic rock. To qualify technically as a *sand* the particles must fall within arbitrary size limits, from $\frac{1}{16}$ to 2 mm. If smaller, they comprise *silt*, if larger, *gravel*. Among the sand grains, the larger ones become blunted or rounded by abrasion as they are transported downstream at every freshet. Originally they are hexagonal crystals, but the edges and points become first dulled, then rounded as they are rolled along and banged against one another and against rocks in the stream bed. Within broad limits, one may estimate the distance such grains have traveled by the amount of wear they show. The smaller grains are protected by a buffer action of the film of water surrounding each, and they remain angular.

The sands of the sea, since they will have traveled long distances in most cases, will show more abrasion than those of rivers or brooks. Also they will generally display a greater mixture of minerals, since they draw upon a whole watershed for their source lands. In a typical ocean beach sand, quartz will predominate, but there will be brown grains of *monazite sand*, a thorium-bearing mineral, on Carolina shores, and in many places, black *magnetite sand*, an iron ore whose grains respond to a magnet. *Garnet sand* will exhibit dark red grains; if it is sufficiently pure, it may be used in making abrasive papers. In most regions ocean sand will also include fragments of organic origin—bits of shells and corals and, most interesting of all, diatoms, Foraminifera, and Radiolaria, though usually not all these kinds of fragment in any one place. Indeed, this sand is a veritable Pandora's box of surprises for the microscopist (Fig. 54).

The sands of the desert are very different from those of the sea. One doesn't have to go to the Sahara or Arizona, however, to examine the effects of abrasion by wind instead of by water. Back of the strand along many a stretch of both ocean and lake are dunes—collections of sand made by wind action. If not too heavily covered by vegetation, a dune will reward the observer by a demonstration of how it gradually moves; it is literally rolled over and over by the prevailing wind. Sit on the top for a few minutes and focus your attention on a few sand grains on or near the top; here and there, a few at a time when the wind is moderate, a grain will be blown over or from the top and roll down on the lee side. There is no buffering action of water films, and all the grains tend to become fine in size and perfectly rounded in form. On a flat desert the wind rolls the sands along like miniature bowling balls, and the sandstorm carries them aloft, where they become tools that blast away at exposed rocks and carve them into fantastic shapes. Wind-blown soil may be carried long distances and pile up as deposits called *loess*, immense exposures of which occur in the Missouri Basin, north-central Europe and Asia, and eastern China. The sand grains of loess testify to their means of transportation; they are fine and spherical.

Among other soils are *volcanic ash*, a fine deposit that much resembles ashes from fires; clay, composed of silicates of

Fig. 54. Ocean beach sand, a puzzle for the microscopist.

Fig. 55. Two styles of geologic hammer. (Courtesy Ward's Natural Science Establishment, Inc.)

aluminum, an extremely fine soil that is deposited in the form of silt and mud; and *loam*, a mixture of sand and clay. The sand makes loam more porous, the clay less so; if the two are in proper balance, water will drain through loam slowly, and enough will be held for plant roots. In popular usage, loam also includes *humus*, the organic part of a rich soil, derived from animal and plant remains and excreta and abounding in soil bacteria.

To prepare the finer soils for microscopic study, mix a small amount with some 100 times the volume of water, stir or shake well, then with a pipette place 1 large drop of this suspension on a slide and allow it to dry completely; add mountant and cover glass. As with sand mounts, the particles must be sufficiently dispersed to permit analysis. Pure white clay is *kaolin*, from which porcelain is made; red clay, so abundant in the Southern states, usually owes its rich coloring to rust, literally, for it contains oxides of iron. There are yellow clays, blue clays, and others; they all result from the decomposition of aluminous minerals, especially *feldspar*, another of the principal components of granite but one that is commonly mingled with impurities.

If one is to do much collecting of rock, mineral, and fossil specimens he will need a *geologic hammer* (Fig. 55), the face square for trimming, and the peen either a horizontal cutting edge or a pick. An old hatchet will do for a trial trip or two. For soil samples a large auger or the ordinary brace and bit will be found useful; one can bore down into the soil and then jerk up the core with this tool.

The dump heaps of mines, either active or abandoned, and the pits of quarries are favorable hunting grounds for the geological collector. Railroad and highway cuts through hills and the stream valley or gorge will show exposures where rocks are seen lying beneath the soil, as well as outcrops where they come to the surface. Minerals will be found principally as components of rocks or as veins running through rocks. Help in assembling specimens may be obtained from local Grange officers, county agricultural agents, state geologists, or perhaps from a local rock and mineral club. Samples or slides may be purchased, and there are popular magazines devoted to mineral and rock study, through the medium of which you can locate other interested persons who wish to buy, sell, or exchange.

The study of either rocks or minerals is complex, and determination of kinds is often difficult. Many approaches are possible: there are physical tests (e.g., for hardness, luster —whether metallic, vitreous, or greasy—color of the streak left behind when the mineral is rubbed across a streak plate of unglazed tile); there are chemical tests (limestone effervesces with acid); but above all in importance are the optical tests with the microscope. A tiny quartz crystal forming a portion of a piece of granite becomes a huge and glittering object when magnified; identification is greatly aided by the ordinary compound and especially by the wide-field binocular microscope. Small pieces, broken up with a hammer, can be affixed to slides with a mountant, uncovered, and studied by incident light. However, a better, protected, and more permanent mount is made by either the cell or box methods.

Slide rings made of glass or plastic may be purchased in various diameters, and we have used bone embroidery rings and small brass curtain rings (Fig. 56). Clean a slide with extra care; cut a piece of black photomount paper by tracing

Fig. 56. Cell mount made with bone embroidery ring.

124

Fig. 57. Homemade turntable.

around the inside circumference of the ring to be used; fasten this paper disk to the center of the slide with Duco cement; coat the bottom surface of the ring with the cement and allow it to dry, then coat it again and, while it is still tacky, attach it to the slide so that it completely and accurately encloses the paper; place a light weight on top of the ring and allow it to set thoroughly. If the cross section of the ring is a circle, as with bone and brass rings, rub down both top and bottom surfaces with a file or hone so that a flat area develops for cement contact purposes. Such ring mounts may be prepared a dozen at a time and stored in a dust-free receptacle until needed.

A small piece of rock or a cluster of mineral crystals is now fastened to the black paper inside the ring with the cement, making a *cell mount*, the space within the ring being likened to a prison cell. Store until perfectly dry, or warm very gently. Then flame a circular cover glass of proper size and seal it on with either the cement or a regular mountant. This completes the slide, but most workers prefer to double seal the cover by *ringing* it. This is customarily done by dipping a fine-tipped brush in gold size, asphaltum varnish, or a lacquer, and spinning the ring by means of a *turntable*. The operator rests his wrist on the heel of the table, the brush poised over the slide, which is centered on the revolving disk and held in place by spring clips, then gives the wheel a spin with a finger of the other hand, lowers the brush to make contact, and applies a coating to seal the cover glass to the ring. When this is dry, a second coat is spun, and so on until the desired thickness is attained.

The turntable may be homemade, of wood (Fig. 57), but

one of our correspondents has sent in a suggestion for a gadget that is easier to make and handier to use. He fashioned a small block of wood with a central hole to fit over the axle of the turntable of a phonograph. Two spring clips held the slide, and a bridge of wooden strips across the entire table provided a hand rest.

Not only are cell mounts sealed; the cells themselves are often made in this way. For example, a shallow cell is wanted in a mounting of the minute shells of the Foraminifera; build up a wall of balsam, cement, or lacquer by applying successive coats until the proper height is reached, then affix the cover to the last coat while it is still tacky. When dry, spin one or more finishing coats to seal the cover. Craftsmen at microtechnique seal all their slide preparations; this sealing adds nothing to their utility and does take extra time and effort, but it improves permanence and adds considerably to appearance.

The second method of presenting geological whole mounts is to use small square pillboxes, obtainable at pharmacies. The interior of the box is painted a dead black, and the bottom half is then cemented to a slide. A small pyramid of cork is cut to such a height that, when the specimen is cemented to the apex, it will be approximately flush with the top edge of the uncovered box. The cork is cemented to the box bottom and the specimen to the cork. This type of mount has the advantage that full relief of the crystals against an illuminated black background is provided—a wonderful sight under low magnification—and the box top is used to cover the mount for protection. Identifying data are written on the lid, and the side of both lid and box are given the same serial number, so that there will be no danger of mixing lids. If preferred, the specimens may be mounted in such boxes and not on slides, the boxes forming the collection.

Among attractive mounts by either method are small bits of native gold, silver, and copper, diamond chips, crystals of the semiprecious jewelry minerals (amethyst, topaz, opal, garnet, turquoise), clear quartz, rose quartz, smoky quartz, opalized wood, the brilliantly colored malachite and azurite, sunstone, and many others. The small amounts needed for microscopy may be secured from dealers at little expense.

The slide mounts thus far described will aid in identification of mineral crystals and hence of the rocks that contain them. But for professional work they are inadequate. It may be necessary not only to look at a crystal and see its form and color, but also to determine its optical properties, using polarized light, and for this one needs the most highly specialized of all forms of microscope, the *chemical,* or *petrographic, microscope* (Fig. 58). This expensive instrument has a circular stage, to permit rotation, a vertical illuminator, polarizing elements, and numerous extra devices to modify the illumination.

Geologists use thin-section slides (Fig. 59) of rocks, min-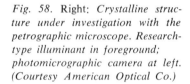

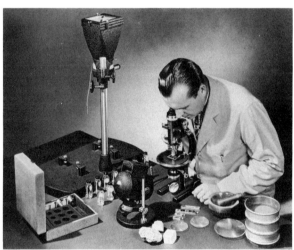

Fig. 58. Right: *Crystalline structure under investigation with the petrographic microscope. Research-type illuminant in foreground; photomicrographic camera at left. (Courtesy American Optical Co.)*

Fig. 59. Below: *Thin rock section of oölitic limestone, containing fossils, 41×.*

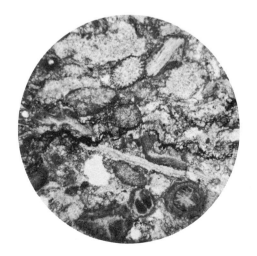

erals, fossils, and meteorites for analysis of composition, employing all the methods of lighting. To be sure, a rock, like a bone or a tooth, cannot be cut on a microtome as can soft organic tissues (Chapter 12); "sectioning" in this case means sawing a very thin disk, then grinding down pieces the size of a postage stamp on an emery wheel or between two hones. The completed specimen must be thin enough so that fine print can be read through it; then it is rinsed in ether to get rid of the trash, and mounted. No xylene is used, but it is often necessary to weight the slide with a few small coins to prevent the specimen from curling.

Fossils

Aside from thin sections of portions of larger fossils, there remain for mention here the microfossils—the Foraminifera and Radiolaria of the class Sarcodina (Protozoa) and diatoms of the Algae. The deposit in which fossil diatoms occur is known variously as diatomaceous earth, infusorial earth, or kieselguhr. Inasmuch as the mounting methods are the same as for recent species, i.e., those of the present geological age, discussion is deferred to a later chapter (p. 168).

Metallography

The microscopy of metal structure is *metallography*, one of the most important of all industrial applications of magnification. The microscope, teamed with the camera in a professional though easily copied outfit termed a *metallograph* (Fig. 60), is the boss of the vast empire of steel, and operators of

Fig. 60. A metallograph, designed for visual projection and photography. Specimen under study is similar to that shown in Fig. 61. (Courtesy Bausch & Lomb.)

such assemblies, *metallographers*, are always in demand. Since this branch of microscopy is far less complex than the medical, it should not be overlooked by those preparing for a professional career.

For an adventure in metallography we shall visit the tinsmith, machine shop, repair shop, and garage, as well as the dime store, after exhausting home resources. What we shall be seeking are small pieces of various metals: not only copper, tin, zinc, nickel, and iron, but such alloys as bronze, brass, and steel, and especially different forms of steel, such as nickel steel, chromium steel, and others.

The general method consists of cutting metal specimens to a convenient size (one that has been widely adopted is a square with a surface ½ by ½ in. and a thickness of ⅜ in.), grinding until they are smooth and flat to the unaided eye, polishing until they are microscopically smooth, then etching with either weak acids or bases. These reagents attack some of the constituents more than others and thus throw the crystal structure of various components into relief. Then the specimens are studied by incident light and moderate magnification, or they are photographed and the prints or enlargements are studied, or positives are prepared as lantern slides for projection and hence further magnification. Details of structure invisible by other means become clear, and the knowledge so gained has greatly influenced procedures in smelting, alloying, treatment, and utilization of metals.

Rough out the selected piece of metal with a hacksaw or snips, and place it in a vise if possible. Use one or more files, decreasing in coarseness, to shape the piece as a whole, as well as to begin smoothing the surface to be prepared. Bevel the edges to a 45° angle where the four sides meet this surface. The filing, as well as all subsequent grinding and polishing operations, is performed differently than with nonmetallic subjects, being always in one rectangular direction only, and never rotary or irregular. Moreover each successive step is done at right angles to the one preceding, until the scratches made by the first are completely removed by the second. Thus, if the first filing is done in what, for purposes of description, we shall call the north-south direction, then the second is east-west, the the third is north-south, and so on.

With the filing completed, most technicians prefer to set the metal firmly in a block of wood, of a size easy to grip with the hand, about ⅛ in. of the selected metal surface protruding. Various papers are then employed to continue the smoothing procedure. Emery, sand, carborundum, and still other papers are available at low cost and in grades of fineness indicated by numbers, 6 or 7 being coarse, 2 or 3 medium, and 0 and 00 fine. Three grades will usually suffice. These papers should be tightly stretched; one method is to cement them firmly to some perfectly smooth and hard surface, such as hardwood, plate glass, or steel plate. Rub the metal surface on the paper, decreasing the hand pressure as the abrasive becomes finer, and examine the specimen with a hand magnifier to determine when the scratches made in the previous rubbing have been removed.

Next comes polishing—actually a continuation of the grinding, but done lightly and with such fine abrasives as powdered rouge. Begin with coarse rouge, then pass to fine, or secure a graded series of levigated alumina, adjusted to the hardness of the metal being processed. Probably the best medium for holding these fine materials is a small piece of clean, damp chamois, stretched tightly over a block of hardwood and secured by thumbtacks. After each operation, wash the metal and the chamois thoroughly, so that no particles of a coarser abrasive will be carried over into a finer one. Remember each time to alternate the direction of rubbing.

When the finest rouge or aluminum has been employed and the metal piece washed and dried, it should be perfectly smooth and bright, like a mirror. Remove the metal from the wooden block and handle it thereafter with a forceps, grasping it by the sides only. Avoid touching the shining surface with the fingers or any implements.

Most specimens will now require etching with weak acids or alkalies. Light rays falling on an etched metal surface will then not all be reflected in parallel, as from a mirror, but will suffer scattering and hence reveal outlines of components that would be entirely hidden in a merely polished surface. The etching process is like developing a photographic negative; both bring out the structure that is there but concealed.

Using forceps, dip the metal block into the etching solution for fifteen to twenty seconds, then wash it at once in distilled water, swirling the specimen about to remove all traces of the etchant. Examine the block microscopically to see if it is sufficiently etched, and if not, repeat until it is satisfactory. For iron and steel there are a great many etching formulas, including 10 per cent solutions of nitric, hydrochloric, chromic, and picric acids, nital, ammonium persulfate, and others listed in works on this subject; for copper and its alloys, such as brass, 50 per cent ammonia in water or 10 per cent caustic potash is used. Often heat treatment alone will reveal crystalline structure, while the polished plates of cast irons are examined unetched, without any treatment. A manual on metallography is needed by those who go beyond the introductory stage.

To examine the block under the microscope, one convenient method is to affix the block to a glass slide with Plasticine. In order to make certain that the block is at a perfect right angle to the optical axis, place it first face down on an absolutely clean and polished piece of plate glass. Surround it with a metal or glass ring that is a trifle higher than the thickness of the object; or use two wooden blocks of appropriate height, one on each side, cut from the same piece of polished hardwood so as to be exactly equal in height. Now place a small lump of Plasticine in the center of a slide, and invert this over the ring or blocks, pressing down firmly. Lift the slide up, carrying the metal specimen with it. For storage, keep specimens or slides in a glass jar or metal box in which is a small container filled with calcium oxide, to prevent rust. Change the oxide from time to time, when necessary.

Filings, wires, and other small metal objects may be ground, polished, and etched by arranging them within a small mold, using a magnet to aid in orientation if necessary, then filling the mold with molten Wood's metal. When cold, the entire block is processed as previously described. For those who are sufficiently interested in this adventure, there are commercial grinding and polishing machines on the market. These are electric-power-driven and perform the work easily and quickly.

The purpose of this technique is to determine the minerals present and the size and distribution of their crystals, information of the utmost importance in the metal industries. One of

Fig. 61. Polished and etched section of brass, 30×.

the ends sought is control of the manufacturing processes, an outstanding example being the heat treatment applied to the various steels, on which depend many of the qualities desired. The problem of adulteration is another; even very small amounts of foreign elements radically alter the behavior of a given metal when in use. Again, there is the post-mortem study of fractures in metals with a view to preventing similar errors in the future. Alloying is a fourth important consideration.

Meteorites constitute a study of great interest, since they are the only visible objects from outer space. They are of two classes, the *irons* and the *stones*, and are prepared for microscopic observation by the appropriate method already described; the iron meteorite as a metallographic subject, and the stone one ground down to a thin rock section.

Figure 61 shows a polished and etched section of brass under moderately high magnification and resembles a cubist's nightmare. To the metallographer, however, it indicates a satisfactory degree of blending of the components of this alloy. Figure 62, cast iron, displays a construction called *pearlitic*, interwoven with graphite flakes, and Figure 63 pictures hot-rolled tool steel, with coarse pearlitic structure—the alternation in bands of two forms of iron known as cementite and ferrite.

Chemistry

Aside from its use in analysis, the microscope may also reveal, for those interested in chemistry, the startling picture of *crystallization*. To observe this phenomenon, add common table salt, sodium chloride, to a small amount of hot water, until no more will go into solution. At a given temperature, a certain volume of water will dissolve just so much salt, the fluid being then termed a *saturated solution*. Furthermore, hot water will generally dissolve more of a particular solid than will cold water. Thus 100 parts of water at 0°C. (Centigrade) will dissolve 35.5 parts of sodium chloride, while at 100°C. it will take up 39.6 parts. This is but a slight increase in solubility (12 per cent) when contrasted with that shown by saltpeter (potassium nitrate); 100 parts of water at 0°C. will dissolve

Fig. 62. Fine pearlitic structure and graphite flakes in cast iron, 430×.
(Courtesy Bausch & Lomb.)

132

13.3 parts of saltpeter, while at 100°C., the same volume of water will take up 246 parts, an astonishing gain of 1,750 per cent.

If now we allow a saturated solution to cool, it will contain more than the normal full amount of salt for that temperature, or if we reduce the volume through evaporation the same will be true; the solution is then *supersaturated*. In the presence of any of the undissolved solids this supersaturated solution will precipitate crystals of salt and thus restore equilibrium. The forming of the new solid is crystallization; it will take place according to one of six geometric *systems*. Place a drop or two of your hot saturated salt solution on a slide, cover, and observe under low power with the light cut down. Sodium chloride crystals will form as cubes of various sizes. Seeing them pop out of the transparent, homogeneous liquid is like witnessing a magic trick.

Crystallization can be observed with a great variety of chemicals. Procure a small bit of roll sulfur from the drug store and place a piece the size of a match head on the center of a slide. Heat carefully over a low flame until the sulfur is melted, avoiding inhalation of the fumes. Place the slide under the microscope, add a cover glass, and watch the formation of long, needlelike crystals. Carbolic acid, crystalline when pure at room temperatures, can be treated in the same manner. Permanent mounts of most chemical crystals are made simply by adding mountant and a cover glass when the crystals are thoroughly dry. Some substances, like the elaborate and gorgeous crystals of hippuric acid and other organic acids will dissolve in balsam but have been successfully mounted in castor oil, the slide then ringed for permanent preservation. Figure 64 is a photomicrograph of a chemical crystal slide.

Fig. 63. *Coarse pearlitic structure in hot-rolled tool steel. The bands are cementite, the remaining substance ferrite. Nital etch, 430×. (Courtesy Bausch & Lomb.)*

Physics

Some of the states of matter, more or less taken for granted by most of us, will become much clearer after inspection under the microscope.

Fig. 64. *Crystalline structure of asparagine as seen by polarized light, 11×.*

MIXTURES AND SOLUTIONS First let us mash up a particle of rouge in water—or we may use sand or clay or levigated alumina, lamp black, or India ink. Under magnification it is seen that no matter how finely we may divide these particles, they still retain their identity and will not disappear in the water, as do salt or sugar. The material is *insoluble,* and the mixture is a *suspension*, a merely mechanical arrangement.

Now take a test tube half full of water and add a little oil or butter. As we know, the oil will float on the water, having a lighter specific gravity. Place the thumb over the mouth of the tube and shake violently for ten or twenty seconds; the oil is separated into many small globules, dispersed throughout the water. Examine a drop microscopically. Upon standing, however, all the drops run back together again and once more the oil floats on top. But if we put the tube in a shaking machine, we shall disperse the oil so thoroughly that the droplets become microscopically minute, as your instrument will prove, and will remain apart, a surface-tension phenomenon. Mayonnaise represents this state of matter, the *emulsion*, and a thin smear examined microscopically will stand in for the machine-shaken oil and water, not available to everyone. Another good illustration is to compare ordinary milk and homogenized milk on two slides, the latter being also an emulsion, the butterfat being so finely dispersed that the cream will not separate out.

Surface tension is due to molecular forces pulling the surface film of a droplet inward, resulting in a tendency to round up the substance and keep it in spherical form. It increases as the volume diminishes, and hence there arrives a volume, as we break up the droplet into ever smaller subdivisions, in which this tension is great enough to keep adjacent droplets apart and prevent their running back together.

Another important physical topic will be demonstrated when you view a fine suspension, as of carmine particles in water, or the emulsion of homogenized milk. Ignore the larger masses or droplets and look for the very finest ones, with high power and moderately dim light. They will be seen in motion, performing a series of dancing movements. The explanation of this weird performance is that the particles are being bombarded by the invisible, ultramicroscopic molecules of the water and are knocked first this way, then another, so that they oscillate, or vibrate, back and forth and up and down, a behavior known as *Brownian movement*. Thus, although we cannot see the water molecules, their presence is made known by their effect on the visible particles. This observation under the microscope aids in an understanding of the important concepts of diffusion and osmosis.

Emulsions are also a form of *colloid,* other examples being gelatin, starch, and albumen, the particles ranging in size downward from the microscopic to the molecular; you will not be able to see any particulate matter if some white of raw egg is examined microscopically. Below this state comes that of the true or *physical solution,* in which the mixture of two or more substances is at the molecular level. Alcohol and water will mix in any proportion: thus you can dissolve water in alcohol or you can dissolve alcohol in water—it is merely a matter of which predominates. The two can be separated, though never quite completely, by *fractional distillation,* since alcohol boils at a lower temperature (78.3°C.) than water (100°C.) and thus can be converted to vapor, drawn off, and condensed back to liquid alcohol, while the water remains in the liquid state.

A *chemical solution* is one accompanied by a chemical change, as when silver is dissolved in nitric acid; the substance that goes into solution in this case is not silver, but silver nitrate, a reaction taking place between the solvent and the solute. Finally, there is the *electrolytic solution,* e.g., solution of salt and water. When sodium chloride is placed in water it not only *dissolves,* in the sense that the particle size becomes molecular, so that the salt molecules are intermingled with the water molecules, far below the level of even microscopic visibility, but it also *dissociates* into atoms carrying unit electrical charges; such atoms are known as *ions.* Thus sodium chloride is *ionized,* the sodium atoms carrying positive charges (Na+) and the chlorine atoms negative ones (Cl−). This sort of solution will carry an electric current and constitutes an *electrolyte.* The remarkable fact, when salt is dissolved in water, is that the salt no longer exists; there are only separate ions of sodium, a metal, and chlorine, a greenish gas.

An interesting observation of the violence with which two liquids can mix may be made if a drop of water is placed on a slide, covered, and focused with dim light. A few fine carmine particles will permit focusing and also dramatize the effects of the experiment. Add a drop of strong alcohol (95 or 100 per cent) at the edge of the cover and note the powerful *diffusion currents* thus established. The two reagents mingle rapidly, with a force that can damage tissues on a slide if we pass directly from water into one of the higher percentages of alcohol; this observation points up the wisdom of going through a graded series of alcohols, each of increasing strength, as we shall do with organic tissue preparations.

The science of the microscope itself lies in the field of *optics,* a major division of physics. There are on the market kits of those three basic optical parts, mirrors, prisms, and lenses, together with instructions on what to do with them, singly and in combination.

ATOMIC WARFARE Still another interesting performance in the field of physics is this one. Set up your microscope at night in a room that can be completely darkened; with the microscope lamp on, place a wrist watch on the stage of the instrument and focus with the 16-mm. objective and highest eyepiece on one of the luminous numerals. The paint used on the dial figures and the hands contains radium salts. Turn off the lamp and remain seated for a few minutes to allow your eyes to become fully dark adapted, then look into the microscope and see the startling and beautiful fireworks—the visible effects of atomic disintegration.

References

Croneis, C., and W. C. Krumbein, *Down to Earth,* University of Chicago Press, Chicago, 1936. Fine, fully illustrated account of geologic processes and history for all classes of readers.

Fenton, C. L., and M. A. Fenton, *The Rock Book,* Doubleday & Company, Inc., New York, 1946. Excellent guide for identifications.

Howe, H., *Introduction to Physics,* 2d ed., McGraw-Hill Book Company, Inc., New York, 1948. Excellent brief text.

Jenkins, F. A., and H. White, *Fundamentals of Optics,* 2d ed., McGraw-Hill Book Company, Inc., New York, 1950. Best beginner's work on subject, both geometrical and physical.

Kehl, G. L., *The Principles of Metallographic Laboratory Practice,*

3d ed., McGraw-Hill Book Company, Inc., New York, 1949. Apparatus, procedures; many photomicrographs.

Kolin, A., *Physics, Its Laws, Ideas, and Methods,* McGraw-Hill Book Company, Inc., New York, 1950. Among best of recent college texts; comprehensive.

Luhr, O., *Physics Tells Why,* Cattell and Company, Inc., Lancaster, Pa., 1946. Answers layman's questions about natural phenomena. (Sold by The Ronald Press Company, New York.)

Pauling, L., *College Chemistry,* W. H. Freeman and Company, San Francisco, 1950. Masterful exposition of all general phases of chemistry.

chapter ten

The land of Lilliput

We cannot, like Gulliver, visit a country where we will encounter tiny human beings. But all around us is the far stranger and more wonderful world of insects. No other group can display half the marvels for the microscope that this one can; insects and their allies are very highly evolved animals that are unexcelled in providing material for slide mounts to demonstrate such important biological laws as specialization and adaptation.

The orders of insects

The major assemblage of which insects constitute a part is the phylum Arthropoda, which also includes crayfishes, crabs, lobsters, shrimp, and wood lice (Crustacea); millipedes, or "thousand-legged worms" (Diplopoda); centipedes (Chilopoda); and spiders, scorpions, mites, ticks, and horseshoe crabs (Arachnoidea). None of these are properly called "insects"; this term refers only to members of the class Insecta, which have three pairs of legs, commonly two pairs of wings, three main body divisions—head, thorax, and abdomen—and which breathe air (except in certain aquatic young stages) through a system of air tubes called tracheae.

Their importance is out of all proportion to their size. A few are beneficial, such as the silk moth and the honeybee and those, like the ladybird beetles and the praying mantis,

which destroy pests; a few are neutral; but the vast majority
are harmful from man's point of view and are in fact his
worst enemy. Myriads of insects eat every form of crop that
man tries to grow, and others eat stored food, clothing, the
wood of dwellings and furniture, forests, and other animals.
Worst of all are those insect enemies which attack man himself,
as well as his domestic animals, and transmit a formidable
number of diseases.

Insects are divided into a large number of orders, mainly
on a basis of just three characters: wings, mouth parts, and
metamorphosis, and it is not difficult for even the beginner
to learn to recognize a great many kinds.

Information on *wings* considers whether or not they are
present, their number if present, and their shape, size, and construction. Advanced classification deals with their *venation*.
The so-called "veins" of the insect wing are actually dried up
tracheae, but their patterns are highly revealing.

Mouth parts are designed either for chewing (grasshopper),
sucking (butterfly), piercing-sucking (mosquito), or chewing-
sucking (bee).

Metamorphosis is a change in appearance, structure, habits,
and sometimes even habitat during the life cycle. The most
primitive types, such as the silver fish, represent the subclass
Ametabola, without metamorphosis. The stages are egg, young,
adult; the young insects resemble the adults in all but size,
as is true of so many animals that are not insects.

The *Heterometabola* have an incomplete metamorphosis,
the stages being egg, nymph, adult, as in grasshoppers. The
nymphs resemble the adults to the extent that anyone would
recognize them for what they are, yet they do not have all
the adult structures. Wings, for example, are lacking; wing
pads gradually form during the nymphal stages but do not
develop fully and become functional until the insect is full
grown.

The *Hemimetabola* are intermediate; the young do not
closely resemble the adults and could not usually be recognized by the uninitiated, yet there is no chrysalis stage. The
young are aquatic and are termed *naiads,* and the stages are
egg, naiad, adult, the latter being aerial. The dragonfly is a
good example; the naiad is a terror among small aquatic crea-

tures, being highly carnivorous and seizing all manner of victims, even including fishes and frog tadpoles, in its powerful jaws.

The *Holometabola* is the highest subclass and includes the great majority of insects. The metamorphosis is complete, and the stages are egg, larva, pupa, and imago. The *larva* does not at all resemble the *imago* (adult), and there is a stage of reconstruction, the *pupa,* in between, during which tissues are actually torn down and the animal is remade. Thus the caterpillar (larva) is a wormlike creature with no obvious separation between thorax and abdomen, no reproductive organs, rudimentary antennae, chewing mouth parts, short and stubby legs, assisted by temporary, fleshy prolegs, and no wings. The pupal stage is passed as a chrysalis or cocoon, and from this emerges an entirely different kind of animal—the moth or butterfly (imago), slender, with sharply marked division between thorax and abdomen, the latter with no sign of prolegs, with a functional reproductive system, long, delicate antennae, sucking mouth parts, three pairs of long, jointed, slim legs on the thorax only, and two pairs of large wings. The following is a list of the chief orders:

Thysanura: the bristletails, silver fish. Biting mouth parts, no wings, ametabolic.

Orthoptera: locusts, grasshoppers, crickets, walking sticks, praying mantises, and roaches. Biting mouth parts (Fig. 73); typically four wings, the first pair leathery, the second membranous; heterometabolic.

Odonata: dragonflies and damselflies. Biting mouth parts; two pairs of gauzy wings; hemimetabolic.

Mallophaga: biting lice, found on both birds and mammals. Biting mouth parts; no wings; heterometabolic.

Anoplura: sucking lice, found on mammals only. Piercing-sucking mouth parts; no wings; heterometabolic.

Heteroptera or *Hemiptera:* the true bugs. Piercing-sucking mouth parts; two pairs of wings, the first pair of which have the upper halves leathery and the lower halves membranous (Fig. 71), and the second pair membranous; heterometabolic.

Homoptera: cicadas (so-called seventeen-year locusts; true locusts are grasshoppers), leaf hoppers, tree hoppers, aphids, and scale insects. Piercing-sucking mouth parts; two pairs of wings; heterometabolic.

Coleoptera: beetles. Biting mouth parts; two pairs of wings, the first pair (*elytra*) being hard wing cases for the second pair, which are membranous and, when not in use, fold transversely and also like a fan; holometabolic, the larvae called grubs.

Lepidoptera: moths, skippers, and butterflies. Sucking (siphoning) mouth parts; two pairs of membranous wings covered with microscopic scales; holometabolic, the larvae called caterpillars.

Diptera: flies. Sucking or sponging mouth parts, or piercing-sucking; one pair of membranous wings; holometabolic, the larvae called maggots.

Siphonaptera: fleas. Piercing-sucking mouth parts; no wings; holometabolic.

Hymenoptera: bees, wasps, ants, and others. Biting and lapping mouth parts; two pairs of membranous wings; holometabolic, the larvae known as grubs.

Other orders are those of the springtails, termites, dobson flies, May flies, stone flies, book lice, thrips, earwigs, scorpion flies, and caddis flies.

Fig. 65. Scraper used in aquatic collecting.

Collecting equipment and methods

AQUATIC INSECTS Handiest of all tools in the water environment is the *scraper* (Fig. 65). The essentials are a galvanized, heavy, rectangular, scooplike frame, heavy screen bottom, and long handle, with guy wires to steady the frame. Held with the scoop down, as in the illustration, this implement is used to rake stream and lake bottoms, pulling the scraper toward you and dumping the contents on the shore, where they are picked over. The *sieve box,* or *screen box* (Fig. 66), is manipulated in somewhat the same manner. The operator pulls it toward him, raking up the bottom, then, holding the box horizontally with screen surface down, he jounces it up and down in the water to get rid of soil, and shakes it back and forth, as the placer miner does in panning for gold. Or the box may be held vertically on the downstream side of a rock while the operator lifts the stone and the current sweeps animals into the box. Such an implement is readily made from a wooden box or from strips of wood, 12 by 18 or 16 by 24 in., for example, the bottom covered with rustproof wire

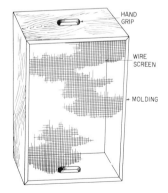

HAND GRIP

WIRE SCREEN

MOLDING

Fig. 66. Screen box for aquatic collecting.

screening secured by molding, and the frame provided with two cut-out hand grips. A heavy-duty fish net can also be used, though one must guard against underwater snags.

Stone-fly and May-fly naiads abound in suitable places in riffles, while dragonfly and caddis-fly naiads dwell in ponds. The huge larvae of crane flies lie buried in creek bottoms; hell-grammites (dobson-fly larvae) cling to the undersides of stones in flowing water and are much sought as bait. Black-fly larvae are fastened to rocks in swift water, even at the brink of a waterfall, while the bloodworms (midge larvae; Diptera) are bottom dwellers in ponds. Mosquito larvae and pupae should be collected. Water boatmen and back swimmers (handle with care—they can give a painful stab with the proboscis) row themselves through the waters of shallow ponds; water striders skim the surface, where also will be noted the gyrations of the whirligig beetles. The big predaceous diving beetle, *Dytiscus,* explores the depths for prey, coming to the surface for air. Water scorpions, looking something like aquatic walk-ing-stick insects, water bugs that carry their eggs on their backs, and the huge electric-light bug, or kissing bug, inhabit ponds and are best hunted at night, using a flashlight. Indeed, the insect life of ponds and streams is abundant and varied.

WOODLANDS, GARDENS, MEADOWS   An *insect net* is essential. Commercial models feature a sectional handle, collapsible frame, and netting of fine material, such as bruxelle, easily torn. If the aim is to secure perfect specimens for mounting in a pinned collection, a fine-net bag is necessary, but for microtechnical purposes any cheap gauze is satisfactory. The frame may be made of galvanized wire bent around a pillar or keg to form a circle about 12 in. in diameter, with the two ends protruding. These ends are wired onto or soldered into the end of a bamboo pole. In netting a flying insect, make a forehand swoop, followed immediately with a backhand, if the first should be a miss. Sweep against the wind, where pos-sible, keeping the bag bellied out. Beware of branches and brambles that snag. When a capture is made, instantly twist the handle so that the bag hangs down over one edge of the frame, sealing off the opening and preventing escape.

The kinds of insects encountered in these localities are

legion: locusts or short-horned (short-antennaed) grasshoppers, the long-horned grasshoppers like the katydid, wood roaches, walking sticks, mantises, bugs, leaf hoppers, tree hoppers, cicadas, and beetles in great array; butterflies, skippers, a great many flies, bees, wasps, and ants. Among true bugs, aphids should be sought for making whole mounts. While *netting* insects is the principal method of capturing them, there are numerous others. Approach a victim that is intent on minding his own business, e.g., a bee gathering nectar, and without haste or quick movements, bring a bottle up from below and the cork or lid down from above, enclosing the animal, including some of the vegetation if necessary, between the two. Even big bumblebees may be taken in this way, which we shall call *bottling,* without danger of your being stung; also beetles and bugs, but flies are too wary. The bottle should be wide-mouthed; it may be a charged *cyanide jar,* though remember to handle this form of insect-killing glassware with due caution for the highly poisonous contents. For micro work, such a jar is unnecessary. Simply place a couple of inches of waste alcohol in the container; this both kills and preserves, initiating the technique procedures.

Under the smaller trees of wood and orchard, spread an old sheet or stand an inverted umbrella, then rap the trunk briskly two or three times with a stout club. Down will come a veritable shower of spiders, bugs, beetles, aphids, ants, and others, which are readily picked up from the sheet or umbrella; this is *beating.* In long grass where there is no danger of snagging the net, pass it rapidly and vigorously through the grass, first right, then left, advancing all the while; this is *sweeping* and will yield an astonishing array of tiny insects, grasshopper nymphs predominating.

Handpicking, with fingers and forceps, is resorted to in many situations. A favorite collector's trick is to turn over flat stones, old pieces of roofing paper, old tins and sign-boards, and the trash in general that often litters the country-side, as well as logs (tearing into rotten ones), bark, leaves, moss, and cow dung. In regions of moist loamy soil the collecting will be good; in rocky, sandy, or dry areas, you will find little or nothing. This method reveals the *cryptozoic fauna* (Greek, hidden animals), creatures that spend most of their time in concealment, some of them venturing forth at night, some at dawn and dusk, and some not at all. According to the section of the country you are in, you should find field mice, moles, and shrews among mammals; small snakes, ground lizards, narrow-mouthed toads, salamanders, spiders, scorpions, centipedes, millipedes, sow bugs (various species also called pill bugs, armadillo bugs, wood lice), and earthworms; and, among insects, ants, termites, dung beetles, woodboring and stag beetles, click beetles, flea beetles and many other Coleoptera, beetle grubs, roaches, crickets, the fascinating mole cricket, earwigs, and (beware!) bumblebee nests.

Parasitic insects should not be overlooked; the farm is the ideal place to hunt them. Hog lice, chicken and turkey lice, botflies and warble flies on horses and cattle, sheep keds, mites —there is a long list of pests of our domesticated friends. Do not overlook the chance opportunity to look over the carcasses of wild animals for their parasites. Hunting and trapping often provide material. Once an entomological friend of the writer had the weird and startling experience of having a huge bald eagle fall dead at his feet, plummeting from a great height in the sky and striking the earth with a tremendous thud! When sufficiently recovered, this scientist searched the unfortunate king of birds and found it crawling with the largest species of bird louse (Mallophaga) he had ever seen. Needless to say, he returned from this successful field trip with several vials full of this rare find.

Insects may be *trapped* (e.g., Japanese beetles may be caught in a special trap), killed with *poisoned baits,* or *attracted to lights* at night. The light trap is used a great deal in professional work. You may find insects in city parks, in the back yard, even in your own home. While autumn is the heyday in the Land of Lilliput, there is no season of the year free from insects. Now let us see what the microscopist can do with all the loot he has collected during this adventure in the open.

Insect whole mounts

If the insect is of suitable size and not too thick, it may be mounted entire, as a flea. Often, as with most moths and butterflies, the larger flies and beetles and wasps, and hosts of others, the specimen is too big to make a worthwhile whole mount; also its parts are usually more interesting as slides than the animal itself. A comparative collection of insect legs, for example, is more valuable as a biological exhibit in adaptation than is a display of the series of whole insects. Insects are generally opaque and often so darkly colored as to mask detail; hence it is customary to *potash* these animals or their parts before mounting.

POTASHING TECHNIQUE   Use a porcelain dish or (in the home) the lid of a baking-powder can for this cooking procedure. Secure a stick of caustic potash from the druggist and add water to make a 10 per cent solution (10 gm. potash, 90 cc. water), or have the druggist make it for you. Be careful with this mixture; handle it as cautiously as you would an acid. Soak the insects in this overnight or as long as two or three days, until the internal organs are digested, leaving only the exoskeleton (external hard parts), which is decolorized and softened, permitting a much flatter mount. With a bit of experience it will be found best to speed up the action by boiling the specimen in the caustic, rinsing it thoroughly in water, and then, with the stick of a kitchen match or the handle of a dissecting needle, rolling the animal gently, from head to tail, just as you would flatten dough with a rolling pin. Whether this is necessary to expel the remains of the internal organs depends on the insect; some experience is necessary in order to modify the procedure here and there. In all cases, when the potashing is completed wash the specimen well in water to check the action of the caustic. It is usually best not to decolorize the insect all the way to transparency but to stop the action when a light brown hue is reached.

A FLEA MOUNT   Whole mounts are made from potashed specimens by the same procedures followed in mounting textiles, with the addition of one further step. Textiles are non-living and perfectly dry; they need neither preservation nor dehydration. But an insect's body will disintegrate unless it is *fixed* against decay. Strong alcohol, for example, is a *fixer*.

Because of its great affinity for water—it takes up water from organic tissues—it is also one of the best *dehydrators* (water extractors); by using a graded series of alcohols, of increasing strength, we may exhaust all but a trace of water from the specimen. Alcohol is also a *killing agent*, so that what are actually three technique steps—killing, fixing, and dehydrating—become just one in that the same reagent does them all.

Catch a flea from an obliging dog or cat, and kill it in alcohol, a cyanide jar, or carbon tetrachloride. Then place it for ten minutes or longer in 50 per cent alcohol (hereafter the alcohols will be designated by A)—70A, 82A, 95A, and absolute alcohol, (100A), then in xylene for another ten minutes, and mount. A long stay, of several days, in the weaker alcohols (50A, 70A) may harm specimens, as the amount of water in the mixture results in maceration. In the higher alcohols (82A, 95A) the longer stay does no harm, as these alcohols are strong enough to preserve tissues. Therefore, after securing specimens, if other duties prevent immediate processing, place the insects in 82A until you are ready, using next 95A, eliminating the earlier steps.

Now repeat the procedure with another flea, this time potashing the animal first, then processing as above. Compare the two mounts and draw your own conclusions. For studying, one may be as serviceable as the other; for photographing, the potashed slide is much superior.

ALCOHOLS   Those with official positions in laboratories of colleges, hospitals, and industrial firms can obtain *ethyl* (grain) alcohol tax-free for scientific work, but others cannot do so, which is a source of annoyance and expense. In recent years several nondrinkable, consequently tax-free, alcohols have come on the market; *n*-butyl alcohol is used in microtechnique, but the best, cheapest, and easiest to obtain is *isopropyl alcohol*. One proprietary brand is *Isopropanol*. There are two grades: the *technical* (90 to 96A) and the more expensive *anhydrous* (water-free). Use the technical grade in making up the alcohol series, and buy a small amount of the anhydrous for the final step of absolute alcohol. Methyl, or wood, alcohol is very poisonous, and it is best to avoid it.

MAKING THE ALCOHOL SERIES Prepare a series *of stock bottles*, labeled for 50, 70, 82, 95, and 100 percentages. They may be from 8 to 16 oz. in capacity, according to the amount of work you intend; any style of ordinary narrow-mouthed bottle will do, but the one for 100A must have a ground-glass stopper. How does one achieve a 70 per cent solution from a 95 per cent one? Sounds like a math problem, but the calculation is done for us by an essential item of laboratory glassware, the *graduated cylinder* (Fig. 67). Fill the graduate with 95A to the 70-cc. mark, then add distilled water to bring the total up to the 95-cc. mark. The result is 95-cc. of 70A. Hence the general rule: fill the graduate with the stronger mixture to the level of the weaker, then add water to bring the whole up to the level of the stronger percentage.

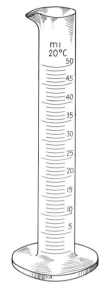

Fig. 67. *Graduated cylinder.*

DISTILLED WATER Since all tap water has flowed over or through the soil, it has picked up salts and is always somewhat alkaline. City water is further altered by chlorination to kill organisms. Laboratory formulas are always predicated on *distilled water*, unless otherwise indicated. Here again the professional has the advantage over the amateur, since his laboratory will be equipped with a still; the matter of obtaining pure water has often been troublesome to the private individual in the past. Fortunately, today there are the bottles of water used by garages in filling car batteries, and most cities now have one or more firms that market a high grade of pure water for those who, for dietary or other reasons, do not wish to drink the city water. These special waters are not very expensive and are entirely satisfactory for our purpose.

A *deionizing filter* to remove salts from tap water is available in the form of a small gadget that is attached to the household faucet. The LaMotte Filtr-Ion Unit (Fig. 68) is inexpensive and will deliver up to about 10 gal. on one charging of chemically pure water of the triple-distilled quality; a refill unit is then installed. This is by far the best solution of the distilled-water problem for the average scientist working at home.[3]

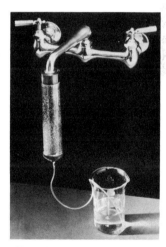

Fig. 68. *LaMotte Filtr-Ion Unit for obtaining chemically pure water.*

[3] Address: LaMotte Chemical Products Co., Towson 4, Baltimore, Md.

ABSOLUTE ALCOHOL   This reagent has such a great affinity for water that it will pick up water vapor from the atmosphere and in a short while is no long 100 per cent. The stock bottle should have a ground-glass stopper, which should be kept coated with a thin film of petroleum jelly to exclude air. The Coplin jar or other container in which this alcohol is used with specimens should also have its lid greased. Keep it covered at all times except when inserting or removing the contents.

A sufficiently pure alcohol may be made from 95A by adding some *calcium oxide* (unslaked lime) in an amount equal in bulk to a peach stone for each half pint of alcohol.

CARBOLXYLENE   This compound offers a substitute method that gets around the absolute alcohol problem. Carbolic acid is another substance that has a great affinity for water and will extract what is left from specimens after they have been in 95A. Melt some crystals over a low flame, taking care to avoid the fumes and not to spill this dangerous fluid, and mix one part of the acid to three parts of xylene. This will remain liquid at room temperatures and will not blister the hands. *Anilin oil* will clear material out of 95A and is preferred by many technicians.

The specimen goes from 95A into carbolxylene for ten minutes and is then mounted; or, if the material is delicate, from carbolxylene into straight xylene for another ten minutes, before being mounted. Or it may go from 95A into anilin oil for fifteen to thirty minutes and then be mounted. This last method bypasses xylene as well as absolute alcohol.

ARTHROPOD MOUNTANT   Turtox CMC-10 (General Biological Supply House) is a nonresinous mounting medium developed primarily for arthropods. The main requirement for use of this medium is that the material be unstained and not too transparent; the main advantage is that the subjects may be placed in the mountant alive or freshly removed from water, alcohol, or glycerin. Old preserved specimens may also be used. No further treatment is necessary, but the slides will keep better if ringed.

148

POSITIONING, SPREADING A textile or mineral mount has no polarity, in the sense that it makes no difference which end or side is up or down, but whole animals do have. The flea should be mounted upside down, with respect to the label, so that when viewed through the microscope he will appear right side up. More important is the spreading of appendages. A mount may display a flea properly potashed, dehydrated, cleared, etc., but if the legs are all jumbled together, if the proboscis is concealed, and one leg is cocked up so that it hides the eye, the mount will have little if any value.

When the insect lies in mountant on the slide, just before the cover is applied, moisten two dissecting needles in xylene and *position* the animal and *spread* the parts. Pull the legs out so that they hang naturally, symmetrically, with the three of the nearest side clearly exposed, without overlapping and with no segments jackknifed in such a way as to conceal parts. Pull out the proboscis in front, if necessary, and spread its parts so that they are plainly revealed. Not until all this is successfully accomplished should the cover glass be applied.

COVER-GLASS PROPS Frequently the material to be mounted, in this group and others, is so delicate that the weight of the cover glass would crush it; or the material is so thick that the cover, for its own protection, must be supported in places around the object. The most used item is a very small bit of a broken cover glass. Save your broken covers in a small box, so labeled, and place three of these, forming a triangle, near the margin, if a circular cover is used, or four, one at each corner, for a square cover. Because of similar refractive index, these bits will be almost invisible in the final mount. If thicker props are needed, cut strips from a blank slide or from cellulose acetate (Fig. 69). If a greater thickness than that of a

Fig. 69. Whole mount of small insect, showing use of cover-glass props.

149   THE LAND OF LILLIPUT

slide seems needed, then make a cell mount instead. The thicker the mount, the thicker must be the mountant; if you have much need for thick mountants keep a separate bottle of thick balsam. It is very easy to thicken balsam; merely let a small amount stand uncovered for a short time so that the xylene evaporates to the desired extent.

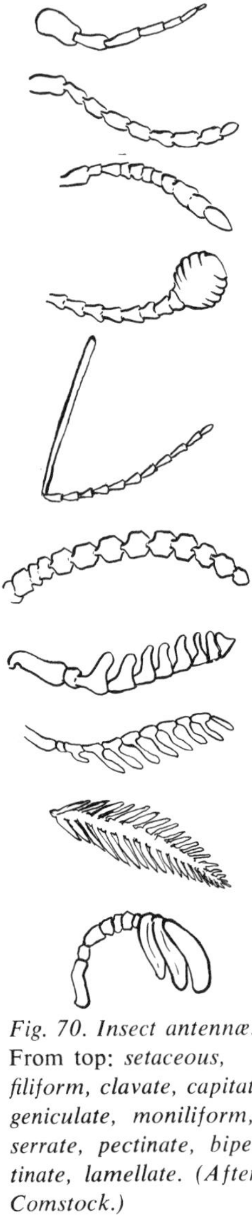

All small insects may be mounted entire; the operator must use his judgment as to whether or not to mount them. He must also decide whether to potash them and if so, to what extent. There are numbers of delicate, translucent, or minute specimens that would be ruined by potashing; there are other cases in which the step is at least unnecessary.

These statements hold also for insect parts, usually more interesting than the whole animals. It is recommended that you make a slide collection of the chief types of antennae, legs, wings, and mouth parts. Wings are never potashed, mouth parts may be, and antennae and legs usually need this treatment. Antennal types (Fig. 70) are important in classification. Legs exhibit adaptation to many kinds of locomotion or other uses, such as walking, running, jumping, digging, clinging, climbing, swimming; the three legs of the worker honeybee display modifications for many ingenious uses. Wings (Fig. 71) provide a major feature of classification, and one mount that is a must is a whole mount of butterfly wing scales, which are modified hairs. Prepare a slide with a thin drop of mountant in the center, hold a butterfly wing above this, and scrape it gently with a knife blade so that the fine scales fall into the resin. The base of the wing usually has the greatest variety of these scales. Look for microscopic hooks (Fig. 72) on the front margin of the rear wing of wasps and bees, and mount the file and scraper apparatus with which the katydid or other long-horned grasshopper serenades the autumn evening.

Mouth parts must be withdrawn with needles. Because of the

Fig. 70. Insect antennæ. From top: setaceous, filiform, clavate, capitate, geniculate, moniliform, serrate, pectinate, bipectinate, lamellate. (After Comstock.)

Fig. 71. Forewing of squash bug, Anasa tristis, 6×. Basal ,half leathery and pigmented, outer half membraneous and veined.

Fig. 72. Hamuli or hooks on rear wing of honeybee.

likelihood of mixing them it is best to process them first. If a grasshopper has been killed in 70A, cut off the head and place it in 95A for three hours, 100A for one hour, and then in either cedar oil or clove oil. These are clearing agents that find special uses in microscopy. After it has been one hour in the oil, transfer the head in a drop or two of oil to a slide, and, preferably with some magnification, such as that provided by a dissecting microscope or at least a tripod magnifier, withdraw the mouth parts with needles. Refer to Figure 73 for the appearance of parts and their arrangement in the mouth. Take off the upper lip, or *labrum*, first, being sure to get all of it. The *mandibles* are hard and black, the *maxillae* and the lower lip, or *labium*, have *palps*, or feelers. The *hypopharynx*, or so-called tongue, should come out last.

Remove each element separately to a clean slide, one at a time, arranging them as indicated in the illustration. When ready to transfer a part, place a tiny speck of thick balsam (or Duco cement) on the slide in the place chosen for that part,

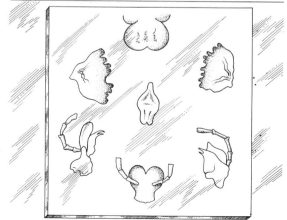

Fig. 73. Arranged slide of grasshopper mouth parts.

then press it into correct position. When all have been trans-ferred, add 2 drops of fairly thick mountant and a cover. Keep the slide perfectly flat for a long time, until the balsam or other mountant is thoroughly set, otherwise the parts will drift. Cockroaches and large beetles also make good subjects for this type of slide.

The proboscis of the butterfly and of various bugs, biting flies, blowflies, and bees is mounted whole, without such dis-section, but the parts may need spreading. In the case of mosquitoes, mount the entire head; slit the sheath of this proboscis with a fine needle, under magnification, and separate the lancets. The same procedure is needed for the horsefly.

The sting assembly

The entire head, the compound eye, the wax plates, and still other features of that most complex animal, the honeybee, may be mounted, but we shall close this chapter by describing the preparation of the *sting assembly*, since this includes stain-ing and brings us to a description of the technique for making whole mounts of organic subjects. Our insect slides so far have dealt entirely with the exoskeleton; when we come to the sting, we must process soft, internal tissues.

Kill a bee by any of the previously described methods, and pull off its head, which may be used for a mouth-parts slide. Place the body in a Syracuse watch glass or other small con-tainer of water for twenty-four to forty-eight hours to macer-ate. Usually such a step is to be avoided, but in this case the rotting in water softens the segments of the abdomen and permits easier preparation of the sting apparatus. After the body has spent one or two days in water, grasp the protruding sting with a forceps held in the right hand and, with the bee still under water, press lightly on the abdomen with a finger of the left hand, at the same time pulling gently on the sting. The entire structure should come out intact. Examine it with a hand lens and compare it with Figure 74 to make certain that the assembly is complete; if any part is torn or missing, discard the specimen and take another bee. It is best to have several soaking at one time to prepare for this contingency.

Pass a needle along the sting sheath from base toward apex

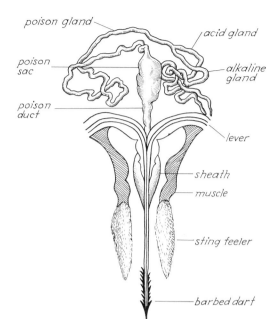

poison gland

acid gland

poison sac

alkaline gland

poison duct

lever

Fig. 74. Sting assembly of worker honeybee.

sheath

muscle

sting feeler

barbed dart

to engage the barbs on the two darts so as to pull them out and expose them, if they are not already fully visible. Prick the poison sac with the needle in several places to admit reagents freely; this prevents air from being trapped in the sac during mounting. With a pipette suck up the water from the container, along with any debris, and remove the bee carcass; replace this fluid immediately with 10 per cent formalin, which should *fix* the tissues for an hour. Liquids may be poured off and on, if one is careful, but the pipette method disturbs the delicate structure less. Rinse in several changes of 50A during fifteen minutes, then work a slide in under the sting assembly, and, with the help of a fine brush, swim this material onto the center of the slide. Place the slide flat, lying across a watch glass, which is now to serve as a slop jar for excess reagents. It is important to note that, once removed from the body, soft tissues *must at no time be allowed to become dry.* A moment's inattention to the duty of adding more fluid will ruin the material beyond recall. Keep in mind that alcohol and xylene evaporate more rapidly than does water.

Stain for one hour in borax carmine, adding new drops from

the pipette as needed, then rinse with water, pipetting it on several times until no further stain is extracted. Drop on 50A, leave it for five minutes, then drop on acid alcohol, adding it until the color ceases coming away freely. While the object is still a bright, clear scarlet, check the destain by washing it off with fresh (pure) 70A, changing this several times, then complete the dehydration and apply xylene. At this point, put on cover-glass props and arrange all the parts of the sting assembly carefully so that, as in the drawing, none overlap and all show clearly. Then add mountant and cover.

Examining the finished slide we may now explain how this infernal apparatus works. The *sting feelers* select the region of the victim elected to receive this unwelcome attention, and then the two *barbed darts* are thrust out of their *sheath* and into the enemy. The darts are worked by *muscles.* The poison is secreted in a pair of long tubular *glands,* one acid, the other alkaline, and goes through a *duct* (the common tube resulting from union of the two glands) into a reservoir, the *poison sac,* where it is stored until needed. The barbs on the darts are effective in lacerating the wound and furthering penetration of the venom, but they seem to us a most defective adaptation in that when the bee stings a larger animal, the barbs usually catch on the tissues, with the result that the whole apparatus, along with the intestine, is pulled out. The bee dies soon after; if only the sting is lost, the bee lives but cannot sting again.

The sting represents a modified ovipositor (egg layer) and is accordingly an organ of the female only. The drone or male bee has no sting. The queen ordinarily uses her sting solely for combat with other queens, so it is the worker bee that does the well-known job on the human subject. The worker is an undeveloped female whose sex organs are nonfunctional.

Other objects to be processed like the sting assembly include the salivary glands of cricket or roach, or their entire alimentary canal, or their nervous system. Soak a cricket in water until the odor is offensive, then pull off the head, whereupon the salivary glands and often the gizzard and even more of the digestive tract will come away with the head. Slit the gizzard lengthwise, flush it out, and expose the inner lining; fix and mount it unstained. The dorsal heart, the entire alimentary canal, and the nervous system of insects must be carefully withdrawn under magnification. Once the part is obtained, the fixing, staining, positioning, and mounting, under large rectangular cover glasses, offer no new problems.

The reagents and apparatus used

Formalin. The uninitiated do not distinguish between *formalin*, a fluid, and *formaldehyde*, a gas. Water will take up to 40 per cent formaldehyde, which is then a saturated solution. It is only 40 per cent of the gas but is 100 per cent formalin. The commercial grade is used in biology and diluted to 5 per cent (5 parts formalin, 95 parts tap water) for preserving whole specimens of vertebrates or their organs, for anatomical work, or to 10 per cent (10:90) for preserving whole brains or embryos and as a fixer in histologic work. If you are to do considerable work, it is suggested that you buy a gallon jug of commercial formalin, then make up your solutions. Do not breathe the fumes of the full-strength liquid, or spill it on the hands or clothing; it is very powerful.

Grenacher's Borax Carmine. Dissolve 4 gm. (grams) borax in 100 cc. (cubic centimeters, the liquid equivalent of grams) of distilled water, then add 1 gm. carmine and heat gently until dissolved. When cool, add 100 cc. 70A and let stand twenty-four hours, then filter and bottle. Objects are stained from water or 50A for several hours to days, depending on bulk and permeability, then passed to acid alcohol to remove excess stain.

Weighing Devices. The introduction of grams, in the preceding paragraph, brings up the question of weighing materials. Every microscopist will have to have some form of weighing apparatus or else have his weighing done for him every time at a pharmacy, which is troublesome and more expensive in the long run. A *chemical balance* of the type shown in Figure 75 is adequate and not too expensive.

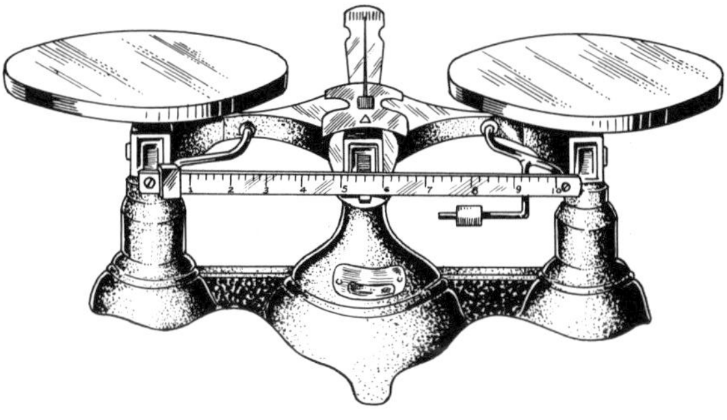

Fig. 75. Chemical balance of a style suited for the microscopist.

Acid Alcohol; Acid Destain. The *progressive* method of staining is that of coloring to sufficiency, then stopping the action by rinsing, and going on to the next step. Better control, however, is attained by the *regressive* method, which purposely overstains, then destains to the desired intensity. Acid alcohol is the usual destain—a 0.5 per cent solution of hydrochloric acid in 70A. Always rinse out the destain by passing to fresh 70A or back into water (according to what is to follow), making several changes. Any acid carried over will fade the stain in time; many technicians therefore prefer to alkalize the first rinse slightly.

Alkaline Alcohol (or water). Make a 0.1 per cent solution of bicarbonate of soda in distilled water. Add 3 to 5 drops of this weak solution to the water or alcohol rinse; larger amounts of the salt are likely to make tissues muddy. Often the tap water of a district is sufficiently alkaline (hard water). Test it with litmus, or get an analysis; if its alkalinity is about that given above, that will be sufficient, and the first rinse 70A can be made up with tap water instead of distilled water.

References

Comstock, J. H., *An Introduction to Entomology,* 9th ed., Cornell University Press, Ithaca, N.Y., 1940. Famous advanced text.

Essig, E. O., *College Entomology,* The Macmillan Company, New York, 1942. Most advanced and complete of modern texts.

Jacques, H. E., *How to Know the Insects,* William C. Brown Company, Dubuque, Iowa, 1947. Fully illustrated manual for identification.

Needham, J. G., *Introducing Insects,* Cattell and Company, Inc., Lancaster, Pa., 1940. Small, well-illustrated book for beginners. (Sold by The Ronald Press Company, New York.)

Ross, H. H., *A Textbook of Entomology,* John Wiley & Sons, Inc., New York, 1948. Best intermediate text on all phases of the subject.

Urquhart, M. A., *Introducing the Insect,* Henry Holt and Company, Inc., New York, 1949. A fine illustrated manual for beginners.

Ward's Natural Science Establishment, *How to Make an Insect Collection.* Small pamphlet of instructions; 25¢.

chapter eleven

Adventuring with smears

The whole mounts we have made thus far have consisted of entire objects (insects), or their parts (wings), or areas of materials having no specific sizes (textiles, metals), or strews of inorganic substances (sand). With the exception of soils, the entities have been *macroscopic*, i.e., visible to the unaided eye. In this new adventure we shall progress to the technique of making whole mounts of microscopic organic substances; these special preparations are termed *smears*.

Blood

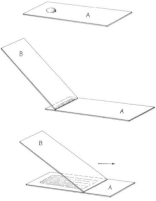

Nearly everyone has, at some time, had his finger pricked by the medical technologist at the hospital and has had a drop or so of his blood smeared on slides. What does she do with them? Why? The answers to these questions will take us into one of the many medical applications of micrology.

Blood smears are just a bit tricky to make, but the technique is quickly mastered with a bit of experience. As seen in Figure 76, a drop of blood is placed near one end of a slide (*A*) and *immediately* contacted with the edge of a second slide (*B*) held at a 45° angle to the first. Note that the blood lies on the side of the acute angle; it promptly spreads across the line of contact of the two slides, by capillarity. *Immediately* the sec-

Fig. 76. Steps in making a blood smear on a slide.

ond slide (*B*) is pushed rapidly along the first slide (*A*), the blood following. Observe that the blood is *pulled* along and not *pushed;* there is no possibility of crushing the cells, and the blood is drawn out into a thin film, uniform all over if the slide was scrupulously clean. Fixing takes place in this procedure by instant drying, which prevents post-mortem changes; the slide is merely propped against some object on the worktable for ten minutes or until thoroughly dry.

Caution must be exercised in obtaining the blood. Sterilize with 95A the portion of skin to be punctured and sterilize or flame the needle. Prick the ball of the thumb or a fingertip and squeeze out one or more drops of blood. When finished, sterilize the puncture with Merthiolate. Speed is of the essence in this work; the blood clots rapidly, and the corpuscles will not resemble those of the circulating blood unless each step is performed with maximum rapidity. The instant a drop of blood appears from the puncture, apply it to the slide and make the smear.

The stain of choice is Wright's. As the making of this blood stain is difficult, it is best to purchase it as a solution ready to use. When the film is dry, put on a measured quantity of Wright's stain (e.g., 1 drop, 2 drops, etc.) and time the duration accurately to one minute. Then, without removing the stain, add an equal quantity of distilled water and allow to stand for two minutes. For example: 3 drops of stain, one minute; 3 drops of water added to stain, two minutes. Drain off the stain, and cover the slide with distilled water. This *differentiates* the stain by destaining. The water will, if allowed to act too long, extract all the dye, but the destaining should be stopped when the coloration of certain cells is right. Blot the film very gently with a piece of filter paper and allow it to dry. If your microscope is equipped with an oil-immersion objective, leave the slide uncovered and study it with this objective only, using oil directly on the smear. Blot gently at the end of each study session. If you do not have this objective, add mountant and a cover glass to the stained and dried slide. The reason for this difference is that the stain keeps better if left uncovered. The smear may be made on the cover glass instead of on the slide. A drop of blood is placed on a cover, which is immediately capped with a second cover; the two are then instantly slipped apart, leaving a film on each. When stained and dried, each is inverted over a drop of mountant on a slide, making two finished mounts.

In studying a blood smear you will be examining some typical cells (white corpuscles) from the body of an animal higher in the scale of life than the protozoa. A *cell* is a mass of protoplasm surrounded by a membrane and containing a central body, the *nucleus*. This part is denser and stains more deeply than the rest of the cell and is usually spherical. If the nucleus is removed by microdissection, the cell dies, showing the nucleus to be essential. The rest of the protoplasm, surrounding the nucleus, is the *cytoplasm*. The protozoa, taken up later in this chapter, have nuclei, but bacteria do not.

A human blood smear properly stained with Wright's stain (Fig. 77) should show a vast array of *blood corpuscles* spread over the field, thinly enough to be countable. Most of them are *erythrocytes* (red cells) or *red blood corpuscles*, and they should be of a salmon-pink hue; longer staining or shorter washing yields bluer slides; shorter staining or longer washing gives redder results. These corpuscles are cells that lose their nuclei during development and become biconcave disks. At first glance they may seem nucleated, but the lighter center (or darker, depending on the focus) is an optical effect due to the lenslike shape of these bodies. They are remarkably constant in size, averaging 7.5 microns (0.00075 cm.) in diameter; advantage can be taken of this fact to make approximate measurements, by eye, of parts of human tissues and organs in histologic studies. The diameter of an artery, for example, can be judged by comparison with that of an included corpuscle. There should be 5 million of these cells in every cubic millimeter of normal male human blood, and 4½ millions in female blood. Their function is to carry oxygen from the lungs to all the cells of the body. This task is performed by the pigment *hemoglobin*, present in the cell cytoplasm as a colloidal mixture.

Here and there one sees different cells with blue nuclei. These are the *leucocytes*, or *white blood corpuscles*, numbering but 8,000 per cubic millimeter, a ratio of one white to every 625 red cells, and their general function is to police the body, engulfing bacteria and foreign matter or bits of worn-out and

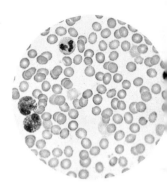

Fig. 77. Human blood, Wright's stain. The two large corpuscles at lower left are eosinophils; at upper left a neutrophil, at right a lymphocyte. Others are erythrocytes.

disintegrating cells. The red cells are incapable of locomotion and are buffeted about by the swift flow in the vessels, but the white cells can put forth pseudopodia and crawl, even against the current. They creep and feed like an ameba and so are said to exhibit *ameboid movements*. Five kinds may be recognized on a properly stained slide, under either a high-dry or (better) oil-immersion objective. First look to see whether or not there are granules in the cytoplasm and, if so, whether they are fine or very large and coarse.

Cells ranging from smaller than the red cells to somewhat larger, practically all deep-blue nucleus, with just a thin rim of robin's-egg-blue cytoplasm are *lymphocytes*, making up some 25 per cent of the white cells. Larger cells with the same color scheme but with more cytoplasm are *monocytes*, comprising only 3 per cent of the white cells. Their nuclei may vary from oval through kidney-shaped to horseshoe-shaped, according to age. The cytoplasm of lymphocytes and monocytes is nongranular, whereas that of the remaining three is extremely granular, earning them the collective designation of *granulocytes*. Most numerous of these is the *neutrophil*, with fine lilac cytoplasmic granules and a purple nucleus that exists in countless forms, typically in several irregular segments connected by fine threads. These cells average 10 microns in size and make up 75 per cent of the leucocytes. They are actively ameboid and perform *phagocytosis* ("I eat a cell"), engulfing bacteria with their pseudopodia. If the granules are large and bright red, the cell is an *eosinophil* (the red dye in Wright's stain is eosin; *phil,* a lover of); they make up some 5 per cent of leucocytes. If the granules are blue, the cell is a *basophil,* the rarest of corpuscles, present only to the extent of 0.5 per cent of the white cells. The nucleus of these is frequently in the shape of the letter S. Small, irregular, clumped bodies between corpuscles are *blood platelets*, which play a part in the clotting of blood.

Wright's stain will also bring out malarial parasites in the red cells; it, as well as other stains, is used for microscopic confirmation of diagnoses of other microbial blood diseases. But laboratory examination of the blood is made primarily for analysis of general body conditions and the detection of pathologic events outside the blood stream. Abnormalities in the blood count may indicate many things to the physician; for instance a pronounced rise in the number of eosinophils may mean that the body has suffered an invasion of the tiny but dangerous worm, *Trichinella spiralis,* the cause of trichinosis. From every standpoint the condition of the blood is of utmost importance to the physician.

Now make an observation of fresh, living blood. Prepare several slides at one time while the finger is being sacrificed. On the first, place a drop of blood and set it aside to dry; on the second spin a shallow cell of petroleum jelly, fill the interior with 1 or 2 drops of blood, and cover immediately, sealing the cover with more petroleum jelly as necessary to exclude air. On a third slide, place 1 drop of blood, cover, and study immediately. It will be seen that the erythrocytes adhere in rows, or stacks, like poker chips; these stacks are called *rouleaux.* You are certain to notice that a single erythrocyte is not red, despite its name, but a faint greenish yellow. Only when the cells are piled up to a depth of several layers does the pigment, hemoglobin, appear red.

As evaporation occurs around the edge of the cover, it will be seen that some of the red cells have shrunk so that their outline has become thorny; these are *crenated corpuscles,* caused by loss of water from the interior of the cells. Now add a drop of distilled water at the edge of the cover, so that it runs under and dilutes the blood; the red corpuscles nearby will swell up and become almost invisible *blood shadows.* In the first case the *blood plasma* in which the corpuscles float has become *hypertonic,* with increased osmotic pressure, and water leaves the corpuscles to enter the plasma, shrinking the corpuscle; in the second case the plasma is *hypotonic,* with decreased pressure, water leaving the plasma and entering the cells. In normal circulating blood, the fluid inside the corpuscles and that of the plasma surrounding them are in a state of osmotic equilibrium, and there is no flow one way or the other.

Follow up this study with an observation of circulation in the living animal. Anesthetize a frog with ether, and set up a demonstration like that suggested in Figure 78. Keep the frog and his cloth wrapper wet, keep the nostrils exposed, stretch a portion of the web of the foot between two pins, and keep that part immediately below the objective wet and covered with a broken bit of cover glass shaped to fit the space. You will be astonished at this wonderful sight.

Returning to the other preparations, the petroleum-jellied slide is used for lengthy studies of fresh blood cells without changes in their normal shapes and for watching the action of leucocytes. Human, or other mammalian, blood will have to be kept at body temperature on a *warm stage* if its white cells are to be seen in action, and those of mechanical and electrical ingenuity will be able to contrive this gadget, but we can more easily use frog blood, which does not have to be warmed. To the third slide, which has a drop of blood that was allowed to dry on the glass, add a drop or two of Nippe's solution, made by dissolving 0.1 gm. each of potassium chloride, potassium iodide, and potassium bromide in 100 cc. glacial acetic acid. Put on a cover glass, and heat the slide gently until it is dry. Remove cover, examine microscopically, and if successful, add mountant and a fresh cover. For those who do not have a considerable chemical stock, it will be advisable to buy a small amount of this solution ready-made.

The successful preparation shows *hemin crystals* (Fig. 79), a positive test for blood. The small, brown, rhombic plates result from interaction of the salts of Nippe's solution with breakdown products of hemoglobin; hence there is no possible source for these crystals except blood. You can place a few drops of blood on a piece of wood, to simulate the floor or furniture; on a textile scrap, to imitate upholstery or rug; later, when long dry, scrape the stains, collect scrapings on a slide

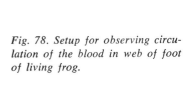

Fig. 78. Setup for observing circulation of the blood in web of foot of living frog.

in a drop of water, then apply the Nippe's solution and prepare hemin crystals as before. The test is used in crime detection practice to determine whether or not a suspected stain is blood.

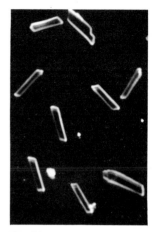

Fig. 79. Hemin crystals from human blood, dark-field illumination.

Bacteria

Introduction of bacteriology as a nineteenth-century science placed the practice of medicine on a scientific basis because of the adoption of Pasteur's discoveries. He found that certain of these very minute organisms are responsible for diseases, in man and various animals, and other investigators later determined the same to be true for many plant diseases. These are the pathogenic bacteria, such as cause the blights and wilts of apples, beans, cucumbers, and alfalfa; the rot of cabbage, and the galls of tomato; the cholera of fowls and hogs, the plagues of cattle and swine; foul brood in the honeybee; and in man, Asiatic cholera, bubonic plague, diphtheria, syphilis, gonorrhea, tuberculosis, leprosy, typhoid, and tetanus. This partial list chalks up a terrific score on the debit side of the ledger against these microscopic plants, arch enemies of mankind. Yet the strange fact remains that we could not live without bacteria! In the nitrogen cycle in nature, plants extract nitrogen from the soil and build it into living protoplasm; animals eat the plants, using the nitrogen for their own cells. But the dead bodies of both plants and animals would lie about on the earth forever, locking up more and more of the available nitrogen as they accumulated, were it not for the third great link in this chain—the bacteria of putrefaction and decomposition, and the series of soil bacteria that return the nitrogen to the earth in a form again usable by plants.

Bacteria are the most widespread of all forms of life, occurring everywhere. Like any other living thing, they must have food, moisture, and a favorable temperature, but wherever these conditions are met, there you will find bacteria. They are classed as unicellular plants belonging to the fungi. In the soil they are most abundant in the upper 6 in., gradually decreasing from there down and becoming rare at 4 or 5 ft. Uncultivated sands may show only some 100,000 bacteria per gram. While this seems like an enormous figure for so small a quantity of soil, it is actually a low count for bacteria because of their extremely microscopic dimensions. Garden soils may contain several millions per gram, and heavily manured or sewage-polluted soils, hundreds of millions.

Rain washes them from the soil into streams, where they may be locally abundant for a short time, but they soon sink to the bottom and die. Sewage carries them to water in vast numbers, but where water has had an opportunity to become purified by the settling of all solid particles, as in lakes and reservoirs, the bacterial flora may fall to a few hundred per cubic centimeter of water. Springs contain the purest water of all. Some bacteria produce resistant *spores* under adverse circumstances, such as drying up of the environment or absence of food. These spores may be picked up by breezes, and thus the atmosphere gets its quota of bacteria, too. The spores float, are freely blown about, and upon falling into a favorable situation, germinate into active cells.

On the skin of man and animals bacteria are abundant, their numbers increasing greatly on the warm and moist mucous membranes of such cavities as the mouth and nose. Between uncared-for teeth they may exist in countless myriads, and it was from this location that Leeuwenhoek obtained the scrapings which, under his microscope, in 1676, revealed the first bacteria ever to be seen and described. In the intestine the ideal assemblage of all the best conditions for bacteria occurs, and here they swarm in greatest numbers. One gram of human feces may contain over 30 millions of millions of them.

STAINED BACTERIAL SMEARS Let us return to our hay infusion, where we first met bacteria. Spores on the dried grass, with probably some additions from the water and the atmosphere, germinated when the hay was placed in water and began to decay. Soon these bacteria, the cause of disintegration, were living with amazing success on the products of their work in decomposing the dead plant material. If you transferred some of them to a slide for observation, you probably could not see very much, even with the light cut down or with an oil-immersion objective—they are so very small and transparent. What is needed is to prepare a film, in somewhat the same way as for blood smears, and then apply a stain to make the bacteria stand out by contrast against the background.

Put a drop from a place containing great numbers of bacteria on a cover glass, cap this with another, and slip them apart, allowing these two films to dry. Meanwhile make a 10 per cent solution of anilin oil in 95A, and shake until dissolved; then add enough distilled water to make the whole a 20 per cent alcoholic solution. Bottle this and label it *anilin water,* to be used in making up anilin stains. Now use 100 cc. of this water with 1 gm. of *crystal violet* (or gentian violet or methyl violet; they are almost the same) as a stain for bacteria.

With forceps pick up the dry film on a cover glass made from the hay-infusion bacteria and pass it, film side up, three times rapidly through the apex of a flame, about one-half second each time. With the cover glass flat, film side up, in a Syracuse watch glass, drop on the crystal violet solution for five minutes, then rinse by allowing a very gentle trickle of water from the tap to flow over it, plunge into 95A for a moment to destain, then drain, blot, flame to complete dryness, and mount.

Another way to study this material is to make a hanging-drop suspension (Fig. 35), sealing the cover with petroleum jelly. Focus on the edge of the drop with low power, then change to high. A still different preparation can be that of Leeuwenhoek, only you will have the advantage of a modern microscope. Mount a drop of saliva on a slide, then scrape between the teeth with a toothpick, and rub up the material so obtained in the saliva. The fecal smear is also easily made: take up a very small bit of feces, human or animal, on the blunt end of a toothpick, and rub it up on a slide or cover glass in a drop of *normal saline* solution, which is 0.75 per cent sodium chloride in distilled water, to make a thin film. The easiest way to prepare the saline solution is to mix 7.5 gm. salt in 1,000 cc. water.

Still other ways to obtain bacterial material are to place a dead fly in a watch glass of pond water and study a drop of this water a day or so later; allow a small piece of raw meat to decay in a very little water in a dish; collect some water from a sewer outlet if one is available; take up a pinch of dirt from the floor or vacuum-cleaner sweepings and sprinkle it over a small amount of water in a watch glass. All these methods will provide nonpathogenic types, suitable for demonstrating all the general principles of this science. It must be emphasized that, in this field particularly, a little knowledge is a dangerous thing; the beginner must never, under any circumstances, play around with the pathogens. He will be flirting with the undertaker, and to no advantage, since the nonpathogens are just as interesting and even more diversified. Until one gets to be a professional, he should handle the dangerous species only under the immediate supervision and instruction of a professional.

Protozoa

Stained slides of protozoans are never so interesting as the living animals, and there is likely to be some distortion of shape, but they do show certain features, such as nuclei, flagellums, and reproductive phases that are seen faintly if at all in the living cells, unless phase contrast is employed. At any rate, stained slides should supplement observations of live material.

MIXED CULTURE SMEAR   Probably the best technique for the beginner is Zebrowski's rapid method, which gives very good results for general purposes. We shall first require Mayer's albumen affixative, which may be bought, or made as follows: beat the white of one egg and, after the albumen has settled to a fluid, add an equal quantity of glycerin. To prevent mold, add 1 gm. salicylate of soda or a few crystals of thymol. Filter the whole through a number of thicknesses of cheesecloth, and since this will take hours or days, keep the filter covered to exclude dust. This preparation is used to affix strews, smears, and microtome sections to slides so that they will not become detached during subsequent treatment.

Make a film of this affixative on a cover glass and on the film place 1 or 2 drops from the chosen protozoan culture, spreading the water over the cover until it is in a thin film, by using a toothpick, broom straw, or cigarette paper and draining off excess by tilting. While the cover is still moist, pass it through a flame, film side up, killing the organisms by heat, and then put the cover face down on the surface of the fixer— hot but not boiling saturated aqueous solution of mercuric chloride in a watch glass.

Mercuric chloride is also known as corrosive sublimate or bichloride of mercury and, as is generally understood, it is

166

a dangerous poison. It may be handled freely providing no part of it reaches the mouth, e.g., from contaminated fingers, as it is only dangerous internally. The salt must be handled with nonmetallic implements, such as plastic or horn spoons, as it corrodes metal badly. It is generally kept in laboratories as a saturated solution in distilled water; 6 gm. will saturate 100 cc.

After fixing for three minutes (if the cover sinks, turn it face up), wash well in distilled water. With the cover face up, pipette on Gram's iodine solution for three minutes, and again rinse in water. Now pipette on a 2 per cent aqueous solution of sodium thiosulfate for another three minutes, rinse in water and stain in borax carmine (page 155) for five to ten minutes, rinse again, then dehydrate rapidly, about fifteen seconds each, in the ascending alcohols. Add enough fast green to the 70A to give it a distinctly green color, and go from 95A into carbolxylene, pure xylene, and mount. Result: nuclei of protozoans red, cytoplasm green. Figure 80 shows a mixed culture slide of stained protozoa.

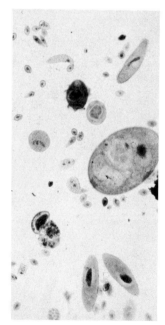

Fig. 80. A mixed culture preparation of protozoa.

GRAM'S IODINE SOLUTION   There are numerous formulas for solutions of iodine. That of Gram is made by dissolving 1 gm. iodine crystals and 2 gm. potassium iodide in 300 cc. distilled water. Some form of iodine treatment must follow any usage of mercuric chloride; otherwise numberless crystals, "mercury pins," will obscure the preparation.

FAST GREEN   This is the first of the large family of anilin dyes to be taken up specifically. They are coal-tar derivatives, their number is almost legion, and they are of every conceivable hue. In general, they may be purchased from chemical supply houses as ready-made solutions, but if the microscopist intends to make many slides over a period of years he should purchase some of these stains, in the form of 10-gm. bottles of the dry powder, and make his own solutions. The method is extremely simple, and there is no sense in paying someone else to do what you can accomplish in a few moments.

Fast green is an intense dye of a brilliant green color. It is soluble in either water or alcohol of any strength, but the preferred mixture for most purposes is 0.5 per cent in 95A.

Action is rapid; staining time is but a few seconds, for sectioned material not over thirty seconds.

Acid fuchsin, anilin blue, basic fuchsin, Biebrich scarlet, Bismarck brown, Bordeaux red, Congo red, crystal violet, eosin, erythrosin, Janus green, Lyons blue, malachite green, methylene blue, methyl green, neutral red, orange G, phloxine, safranin, thionin, and toluidin blue are a few others, some for general, others for special, purposes. Four or five of these dyes are sufficient for a fairly well-stocked microtechnical laboratory, and we advise adding the vials of dry stains as the need for them arises. For special sources in purchasing stains, see the list at the end of Chapter 12.

Diatoms

These, the most important of all the algae for the average microscopist, are found in all aquatic situations, from the ocean to the smallest roadside ditch, and constitute the largest item of the plankton everywhere. They also exist in enormous numbers on the bottom of bodies of water, where they cover soil, rocks, submerged timbers, and such forms of life and its products as the larger algae, corals, and shells.

Collecting. Bottom dwellers are skimmed by using a tablespoon or a piece of used photographic film and going gently over the surface of underwater objects and mud bottoms. Stalks of algae are scraped into a crystallizing dish; floating species are taken in a plankton net. Diatomaceous earth may be present in your vicinity; you can find out from your county agent, state university, or soil conservation official; if not, then small pieces from various localities can be purchased at slight expense from supply houses. Exchanges constitute an important method of adding to one's collections in this group, inasmuch as there are specialists in every corner of the globe, often referred to as "diatomaniacs."

Cleaning. As ordinarily collected, diatoms are mixed with mud, sand, and organic materials and require a thorough cleaning as a preliminary to mounting. Owing to the indestructible nature of silica, diatom *frustules*, as their glass boxes are termed, can be put through an amazingly drastic series of chemical procedures, seemingly certain to destroy almost any living thing, yet emerge unharmed in pristine glory. The living plant protoplast is, of course, obliterated by these measures, but the diatomist wants the shells and not their contents. Each specialist has his own favorite methods in this work, but we have found the one given us by H. W. H. Darlaston, Birmingham, England, unexcelled and herewith reproduce it.

Living Diatoms. Put the scrapings, as collected, into a jar of water. On reaching home, strain through coarse muslin to remove the larger stones and soil particles, then put the strained material into a clean jar and fill with water. Allow to settle for one hour, then put the jar under a tap and turn on a gentle stream of water, flushing for twelve hours or overnight. The stream must be very gentle to avoid washing away the diatoms. At the end, the water in the jar should be perfectly clear, with a fine sediment on the bottom.

Stand the jar in daylight for six hours, at the end of which time the diatoms will be found gathered on the surface of the sediment. Remove them with a pipette, and either proceed to clean them at once or store them in 5 per cent formalin if it is more convenient to do the work later.

When ready to clean, boil the diatom material first in strong hydrochloric acid, using test tubes or other small vessels and small amounts of the acid. Avoid spilling the acid or inhaling the fumes; do the work outdoors or use the fireplace as a chemical hood. Wash in several changes of water by filling the tube, allowing the diatoms to settle, then decanting (pouring off) carefully. Repeat two or three times.

Next boil in strong nitric acid and wash in several changes of water; then boil in sulfuric acid and, while still hot, add a few small crystals of potassium chlorate. This will cause a violent effervescence and must be done slowly and cautiously in an open dish, such as a porcelain evaporating dish. Continue to add the chlorate until the effervescence ceases; then wash in several changes of water, as before, and the cleaning is finished.

There are reasons for these complex measures. The hydrochloric acid kills the plants and removes all calcium salts, the other acids remove organic matter, and the potassium chlorate bleaches. None of these chemicals attacks silica. Remember never to pour water into sulfuric acid, as the heat thus generated is so terrific it might well shatter the container. Do not pour acids into household sinks.

Diatomaceous Earth. Break up the lumps by stabbing them with a screw driver or ice pick, but avoid pulverizing them. Put a layer of small pieces of this earth into a saucepan and cover it with a layer of crystals of sodium hyposulfite. Heat over a flame until the crystals are melted and the earth is fully saturated with the absorbed melted hypo; do not add water at any time. Allow to cool for one hour or so, then add a few more crystals of dry hypo and heat again to ensure thorough impregnation of the earth. Then allow to become entirely cold, when the absorbed hypo will have recrystallized and the earth become broken up to its finest particles by expansion of the forming crystals.

Now fill the saucepan with cold water, producing a muddy mass that will separate in a few minutes into a bottom sediment and a floating scum. The sediment will contain all foreign solid matter and broken diatoms, the scum only perfect diatoms, buoyed up by air trapped within them. Skim off this surface accumulation thoroughly and carefully, as long as it continues to form.

In the remaining cleaning processes, handle the sediment and the scum separately. Wash first with water to remove all traces of hypo, then boil for ten minutes in a strong solution of washing soda. Wash in water, then follow the treatment for living diatoms, beginning with the hydrochloric acid, using a five-minute boiling in each acid. The cleaned diatoms may be stored in shell vials of distilled water, a separate vial for each preparation, or may be mounted at once.

Mounting. There are six principal ways of mounting diatoms according to purpose, and there is an even larger number if they are classified by method. Purposes include locality strews, species strews, type, test, circle, and exhibition slides; methods involve a great variety of mounting media, all of higher refractive index than balsam and glass so as to render these shells more distinctly visible, as well as preparations showing the protoplast.

The *locality strew* is the basic slide. Select a vial of cleaned diatom concentrate from any given locality and transfer a single drop to a clean vial half filled with distilled water. Shake and then examine 1 drop of this dilution on a slide under the microscope to see the number of frustules present. There should be enough diatoms so that many are present and well

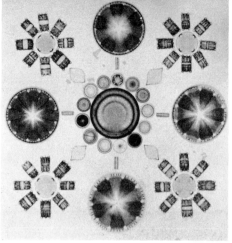

Fig. 81. Diatom exhibition slide, 48×. Each specimen is placed separately, requiring great skill and patience, but the result is an exquisite jewel.

distributed throughout the field, but they should not be so numerous as to form masses and clumps or to lie over and obscure one another. This examination will quickly tell whether to add more diatoms or more water to secure the proper balance.

Place a thoroughly cleaned cover glass on the table before you and breathe on it, then immediately add 1 drop of diatom suspension, which should spread out into an even, thin film. Invert a glass vessel over this cover to protect it from dust while drying. When absolutely dry, put a drop of mountant in the center of a very clean slide, invert the cover over this, diatom side down, and drop it gently into the mountant.

The *species strew* slide is made the same way, but all specimens are of a single species, permitting comparison of large numbers of them and in every position. To prepare, it is necessary to transfer, from a drop of mixed species of a locality collection, each diatom separately to one of a row of vials marked for species. For handling them there are several devices, ranging from a moistened, fine-pointed brush of badger's or camel's hair, a cat's whisker mounted in a wooden handle, to a mechanical finger. The older school of diatomists prided themselves on their possession of and ability to use dexterously a tiger's whisker for this purpose.

A *circle slide* contains selected diatoms arranged compactly in a circle, the number being usually 50, 100, 150, or 200. A ring of ink is spun on a slide with a turntable, the diatoms mounted on the other side of the slide, within the limits of this circle, which is then washed off the finished preparation. Diatom *exhibition slides* (Fig. 81) are objects of great beauty and require skill and patience to construct. The specimens are chosen for their size and shape, to fit into a predetermined geometrical pattern. For both circle and exhibition slides, coat the selected space with gum tragacanth, and as each specimen is transferred by the moistened whisker from vial to slide (or cover glass), breathe on the gum to moisten it. The quick drying following evaporation of this slight moisture sets the diatom in the gum. A newer reagent is Bellido's acetic gelatin, easier to use and less messy than gum tragacanth.

Type and *test* slides are aligned rows of named species, accompanied by a typewritten key to their identity; for example, six in one row; ten in one row; twenty in two rows; and so on. The type slide provides an authentic check, determined by an expert, against which unknowns may be compared. It is like a manual for identification except that the actual specimens are lined up beneath your eye. The test slide consists of a single row, with one to several to as many as a dozen of the species most favored by those testing the resolving power of microscope objectives.

References

Blood: Nonidez, J. F., and W. F. Windle, *Textbook of Histology,* 2d ed., McGraw-Hill Book Company, Inc., New York, 1953.
Bacteria: Frobisher, M., *Fundamentals of Microbiology,* 5th ed., W. B. Saunders Company, Philadelphia, 1953.
Protozoa: See references at end of Chapter 6.
Diatoms: See references at end of Chapter 7.

chapter twelve

Microtomes and sections

The last of the major skills to acquire, in these adventures with the microscope, is the cutting of sections of objects too large or too thick to permit analysis by whole mounts alone. Take the human kidney as an example. It may be examined by the methods of gross anatomy, and it may form the subject of numerous experiments in physiology, but until its microscopic anatomy (*histology*) is explored, we shall find out relatively little about how it operates in extracting nitrogenous wastes from the blood. Before the microscope may be brought to bear on so bulky an organ as the kidney, thin sections that will transmit light must be prepared, and inasmuch as they are then quite transparent and homogeneous in appearance, they must be stained to bring out contrast in the cells and tissues present. The preparation of thin sections of rocks and fossils, and the grinding, polishing, and etching of a metallic surface are, in fact, a form of sectioning, but it is obvious that such methods would not be appropriate for soft organic materials.

The first *sections* were made by hand with a razor, and that technique is still useful. Though we now have complex machines, *microtomes*, to make sections very thin and to make them uniformly and accurately, the original method of *manual*, or *freehand*, *sectioning* is still valuable and should be practiced by all microscopists. We once had a professor of botany who circled his laboratory cutting slice after slice of fresh plant tissues, one for each student, with the greatest of ease and rapidity; some of the giants of an older generation in micrology deplore the decline in training and skill in freehand work among the younger technicians of today.

The cutting implement may be either a regulation barber's razor or a safety-razor blade in its holder, which has the advantage of requiring no lengthy honing and stropping; the blade is merely changed when dull. Young and green plant stems and buds are among the easier subjects with which to begin, graduating to animal organs. Soft objects are held by *reinforcers*, and these include pieces of plant stem pith, turnip, or carrot, and hardened beef liver. For example, a leg muscle from a frog may be surrounded by one of these reinforcers, and the whole bundle cut as a single object; the added material drops away from the muscle when the section is floated in water, but it has meanwhile served its purpose in holding and supporting the muscle. Beef liver is the best of these reinforcers; for this work you should secure some strips about 2 by 1 by 1 in. and place them in 95A for twenty-four hours, than transfer them to fresh 95A and store until needed. Practice cutting this material alone until facility is gained.

The razor is held in the right fist, the specimen to be cut by the left, with the left forefinger held out at a right angle and toward the operator's body. The two elbows are resting on the table, or pressed in tightly to the body, as some prefer. Sections are cut wet, and the action of the razor is that of paring, not that of whittling (Fig. 82). Bring the razor down beyond the specimen, blade flat, edge toward the body, then make a long, sliding, slicing cut, the blade entering the object near the heel of the razor and coming out near the toe. In other words, the razor is not just pushed flat through the object; rather the action is slicing so that the whole length of the blade is used. Cutting is against the right thumb. If anyone is so awkward with tools that he is likely to include a piece of the thumb along with the beef liver, then he is badly in need of practicing this technique in order to acquire a bit of general dexterity.

The razor is kept wet by dipping it into a dish of water or by applying water with a small brush. As each section is cut, dump it into a vessel of water, or float it off by using the brush.

Fig. 82. Method of cutting freehand sections.

174

Do not touch or handle the sections with the fingers or instruments at any time except in using section lifters. Practice this art daily until you can cut very thin sections that are uniformly thin all over; avoid making wedges. Select the best sections for further processing through staining, dehydrating, clearing, and mounting, as described for machine-cut sections. It is well to remember that the thinnest section is not always the best; it all depends on the purpose for which the slice is wanted. Sometimes a thick cut of an organ like the kidney will reveal the general plan of construction better than a thin one, which is in turn better for cellular detail.

Well microtome or hand microtome

After the ability to turn out creditable sections freehand has been acquired, try next an implement called a *hand microtome,* because held in the hand during operation, or *well microtome,* because the material to be cut is placed in a tubular cavity, like a well. The principle is simply that of having some device that will raise the floor of the well a small interval after each cut so that each section will be of uniform thickness. The idea of the screw at once suggests itself. We have seen one that was no more than a very large bolt and nut. The top surface of each was ground very flat and polished until quite smooth; the bolt was started in the nut, and then material—object plus reinforcers—was packed into the cavity of the nut. After each section was cut, the bolt was turned one complete revolution, and thus the thickness of sections corresponded to the pitch of the screw. All well microtomes are no more than refinements of this scheme.

The manufacture of a homemade example (Fig. 83) is not difficult. The cutting plate can be Bakelite or plate glass, the tube a wide brass one, the turning knob at the bottom a radio dial knob. Tissue that has been killed, fixed, and hardened in the usual manner is placed in the well, surrounded by diagonally cut wedges of reinforcers so as to make a tight fit. Some operators use the razor in the paring motion, already described, others prefer to hold the top plate of the microtome vertically, resting on the table, then to employ a chopping

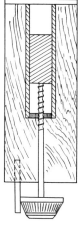

Fig. 83. Top and sectional views of homemade well microtome.

stroke, cutting away from the body and toward the table, running the blade downward with a slicing stroke.

A better system is to embed the object to be cut in the well by using an approach to the regular paraffin technique employed with machine microtomes. A mixture of three parts melted paraffin and one of petroleum jelly, melted together and thoroughly mixed at a low temperature, is prepared. The well of the microtome is warmed and filled with this mass, the tissue is dried as much as possible in a cloth, then put into the well and held below the surface with a toothpick or needle dipped in xylene. When the paraffin mass has cooled and solidified just enough to hold the tissue in place, twist and remove the needle and plunge the well into a vessel of iced water so that the paraffin is chilled quickly, preventing crystallization. When cold and dried, the sections are ready to cut. They are cut dry and processed further as described later in this chapter.

Machine microtomes

Microtome is from the Greek, *small* and *to cut*, and indicates a machine designed to cut exceedingly thin slices. The butcher's automatic meat-slicing machine employs the same principles, on a larger scale, as the more finely made laboratory instrument. In the numerous makes and models there are always two essential parts, the knife and the object carrier, and either of these may be stationary while the other advances a given distance with each operation. The three chief techniques for use with machine microtomes are the freezing, the celloidin, and the paraffin methods; some of the appliances are designed solely for one of these, other implements can be used for two or even for all three. The first type made, and a form still very useful, is the *sledge*, or *sliding*, microtome, in which the object is immovable and the razor is carried by a heavy metal wedge, sliding back and forth in a trough. The knife block is pulled forward by hand, making a slice of the tissue, and is then returned; a micrometer screw is turned through a given arc, raising the tissue block a predetermined amount, then the knife makes another cut. In modern forms of this instrument, the feed mechanism raising the tissue block is automatic.

Models known as *clinical* microtomes and *table* microtomes are smaller and lighter forms of the sliding type. The *freezing* microtome is no more than a glorified well microtome, designed to fasten to a table and leave both hands free. It has attachments to hook up with a tank of carbon dioxide, the rapid escape of which freezes the tissue and embedding medium to permit rapid cutting with a knife formed like a carpenter's plane. Another of the older styles is the *rocking* microtome; this idea has been resurrected and now appears in a modern and simplified version (Fig. 84) that is by far the best microtome for the average amateur, considering cost along with ease of operation.

Universally preferred for routine sectioning in professional laboratories is the Minot automatic rotary paraffin microtome, commonly called simply *rotary microtome* (Fig. 85). A heavy, finely balanced flywheel in a vertical plane is revolved by hand or motor, moving the tissue block up and down, the knife being stationary. Turning the wheel operates the feeding mechanism, a micrometer screw rotated by a large ratchet wheel engaging a steel pawl. By setting a cam, one automatically regulates the number of cogs on the ratchet wheel that will slip past the pawl before it engages, and hence determines the amount of forward motion imparted to the feeding screw for each cut. The great advantages of this machine include the rapidity with which sections may be cut, the ribboning of

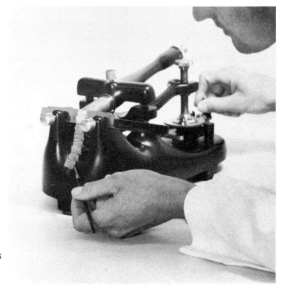

Fig. 84. Forming a ribbon of sections with the Cambridge microtome.

sections, as explained later, permitting serial sections of an object, and the fact that sections are cut dry. The following description of procedure is based on this microtome but is applicable to others with only slight modification.

The paraffin method

Thus far each slide preparation has been a handmade job, an individual performance; but now we reach that division of microtechnique in which the machine takes over and in which slides may be processed wholesale. The steps involved are numerous, and the whole program may seem lengthy and tedious; yet there is nothing difficult about it. Skill comes with practice, and familiarity will make the sequence seem routine. The results of successful efforts will more than repay the labor.

Two examples of method will be given, one for plant and the other for animal materials. They are essentially the same but employ different fixers and stains, combinations that have become standardized through the years and that will afford practice in two different techniques.

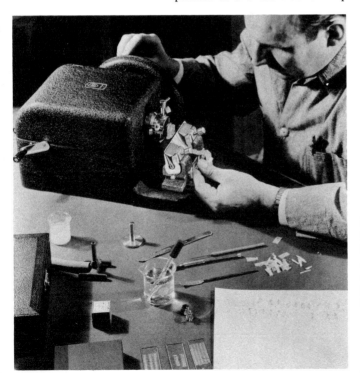

Fig. 85. Cutting sections with the Minot automatic rotary paraffin microtome. Affixed and spread sections on slides in foreground. (Courtesy American Optical Co.)

A BOTANICAL SECTION Cut a ½-in. portion of the stem of any convenient plant and place it in the fixer. The stem selected should be mature, that is, not embryonic or a seedling, but freshly formed and green, so that it will cut readily. Avoid dark-colored, woody stems. Buttercup is a favorite, and so is aristolochia, which is birthwort or Dutchman's-pipe. Clover, alfalfa, young corn, and the green shoots of such trees as basswood (linden) or willow are also widely used.

Fixing. Place the stem in formalin-acetic-alcohol (F.A.A) for twenty-four to forty-eight hours to be fixed, removing at any point between these two limits that will best suit your previously planned time schedule for future steps. F.A.A. is often called the universal fixer. It is good for all general cases, it can be carried into the field for fixing on the spot, and material can be left in it indefinitely without being overfixed. It will fix an amount equal to its own weight, which is unusual; the quantity of most fixers must be many times the weight of the object. Make F.A.A. by mixing 5 cc. commercial formalin, 5 cc. glacial acetic acid, and 90 cc. 50A (alcohol).

After fixing, use several changes of 50A as a wash over a period of twelve to twenty-four hours, then proceed to dehydrate by going through 70A, 82A, 95A, and 100A, thirty minutes each. Next comes dealcoholization, accomplished with xylene: place the stem first in a mixture of equal parts of 100A and xylene, fifteen minutes, then in pure xylene, one hour. Since this reagent mixes with paraffin, we pass next to xylene and melted paraffin, equal parts, for one hour, then into three successive baths of melted paraffin, thirty minutes each.

Infiltering, Embedding. There are numerous paraffins available commercially. A refined product especially for microscopy is carried by supply houses, but many workers prefer Parawax, the chain-store item made for sealing jars of homemade jams and preserves, or the proprietary substances handled by filling stations (e.g., Gulfwax). Probably most widely used today is Tissuemat, a product of Fisher Scientific Company, that is similar to paraffin but does not crack or crumble. It is obtainable as flakes or as cubes.

A most important consideration is the melting point, the desired condition being to have a paraffin that remains liquid at a low temperature, yet becomes hard enough to provide effective reinforcement for cutting at room temperature. Formerly this was a problem in certain regions, e.g., the tropics, or in the northern laboratory in the heat of summer, but the advent of air-conditioned cutting rooms in institutions has largely solved the difficulty. This point should be kept in mind when planning the home laboratory.

A paraffin pot will be needed and may be any kind of ceramic pitcher or glass beaker that will hold as much as a pint. The heat may be supplied by a 40-watt bulb in a student gooseneck lamp that can be lowered over the mouth of the pot. Any form of lamp shade supported over a container for the paraffin will serve. The temperature for the bath is determined by trial and error. The distance of lamp above pot is changed until that one is found where the paraffin at the bottom remains solid but at the top is melted. Objects placed in the pot will sink to the bottom of the liquid and remain there, where the temperature is just high enough to keep the paraffin melted, but no higher. The tissue will be *infiltrated* with paraffin, replacing the xylene, but will not be cooked and ruined.

Inasmuch as one small object placed in a large pot would be more or less lost, there are perforated capsules to lower into the paraffin on the end of a string. Or the pot may take the form of a metal jacket or large container, on the floor of which is placed a number of small porcelain containers or glass beakers, each with partially melted paraffin; a single object is placed in each, permitting simultaneous infiltering of several.

Another device is the paraffin oven. Use an incubating oven or slide dryer (Fig. 86) if the temperature can be controlled within a degree or so, and keep it just warm enough to main-

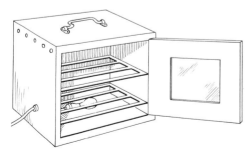

Fig. 86. Small stove-top oven adapted for use as an incubator, a slide dryer, or a paraffin oven.

tain the paraffin, in containers, in a fluid state. It is vitally important that this temperature should not rise more than a very few degrees above the melting point of the paraffin; if it does the tissues will be ruined. Also, when paraffin is overheated, it changes to a state unfit for microtechnical work.

One form of glassware used in this work is the *low form of Stender dish*. In the present example, four would be needed. labeled paraffin-xylene, paraffin 1, paraffin 2, and paraffin 3. In addition, a beaker of melted paraffin should be maintained as a stock, from which the others may be filled. Cut up the paraffin into shavings ahead of time and melt them in the stock jar, to have the fluid ready for use.

The paraffin-xylene mixture does not need so much heat to maintain it in the liquid state as does pure paraffin. Stender dish No. 1 may sometimes be placed on top of the oven, or farther from the source of heat than the other containers. Each of the last three Stender dishes is filled with melted paraffin, nearly to the top. A narrow strip of paper is used as a sling across the middle of each dish, sagging so that when the tissue is placed in the middle, it is supported near the center of the dish, the two ends of the paper crimped over the edges. This ensures penetration of the object by paraffin from all sides and is better than allowing the material to rest on the bottom of the dish. The three containers are kept in the oven or under the lamp, and the object is transferred from one to another, after a suitable time of immersion, with a forceps, spatula, or section lifter. Large, hard, solid, and relatively impervious objects require a longer paraffin bath than do small, hollow, or easily pervious ones: fifteen minutes in each bath is a minimum, one hour an average, and two to three hours a maximum. The stay should be as short as is consistent with thorough impregnation and replacement of all xylene.

When the tissue has finished its last bath, it is *embedded*, a favorite container being a paper boat (Fig. 87). To make the boat, select a rectangle of stiff paper and fold it lengthwise twice so as to divide it into thirds. Fold up each end for a depth slightly greater than that of the two sides. When all four folds are made at once, there result four tab ends at the corners, which are turned toward each other at the two ends, the extra length thus left at the top is crimped down over the

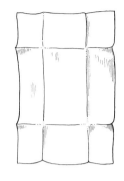
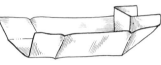

Fig. 87. Steps in the making of a paper embedding boat.

ends and holds them in place. The finished boat should be large enough to hold the object with some room to spare all around. Make a few practice boats and you can soon tell what size any particular one should be. When ready to use, undo the crimped ends and spread the boat out as a flat sheet; write the identification of the tissue on the outside bottom center. Grease the inside lightly with petroleum jelly and reassemble the boat. Pour in melted paraffin to a depth of one-third and allow it to harden just a bit, then warm a forceps and transfer the piece of stem quickly so that no film will form on it. Paraffin solidifies rapidly when removed from its source of heat. Fill the boat with more paraffin, and with two warmed needles orient the object so that its long axis coincides with that of the paper box; hold it straight with the box so that true cross sections may be cut. As soon as the paraffin has solidified so that you believe it will support the object, twirl the needles and remove them and, as soon as a surface film has formed on the paraffin, plunge the box into a beaker of iced water, to congeal the paraffin quickly and prevent crystallization.

When the block is thoroughly cold and hard, remove the paper and examine the wax. If there is a sharp line of cleavage between the top and bottom layers of paraffin, too much time elapsed after the bottom layer cooled before more was added; melt the block and reembed. If there are many and large opaque white spots or areas near the object, this defect too will require reembedding. The spots are caused by alcohol or xylene carrying over into the paraffin; it will be necessary to repeat the infiltering baths and then to reembed. If the top surface of the paraffin block has collapsed on cooling, or if it bulges up in the middle, no harm results unless the object is insufficiently covered. To prevent such an appearance, however, wait a moment longer next time before chilling the block in ice water.

Sectioning. Once embedded in paraffin, the tissue is protected. Such a block may be kept indefinitely, perhaps for many years, before sectioning. If it is to be stored, put the block back in its boat, making sure that all needed data are written on the paper. If it is to be processed immediately, warm the face of the metal object carrier of the microtome, using the alcohol lamp and melting a few chips of paraffin upon the carrier; then warm the butt of the paraffin block and press the two together, holding them tightly for a moment; then plunge the block into a beaker of iced water. After a few minutes, remove, and dry with a towel. Now trim the block by chipping off the paraffin in very thin slices, melting the slices, and applying them to the butt (Fig. 88), smoothing them on just as a mason smoothes mortar with a trowel. Use a spatula or glass rod. Do not carry the lengthwise cuts all the way through, but only past the tissue; leave the butt end untrimmed, and keep building it up. Allow some 2 mm. of paraffin to remain surrounding the tissue. Some workers leave more, some less, and only practice can determine your preference. When a sloping shoulder has been built up all around, place the carrier and block again in ice water to chill it thoroughly, then wipe dry. The tissue may be cut now or at any subsequent time.

Mount the carrier in the clamp on the microtome. Note that this clamp permits motion in three dimensions, and it must be locked tightly in such position that the face of the block to meet the knife is as square as possible, both vertically and horizontally. The long edge of this face must be parallel to the blade. Adjust the blade in the knife carrier so that it has a decided tilt toward the object, about 10° from the vertical, and tighten all clamps securely. Cautiously turn the rotary wheel by hand (Fig. 85) so as to start the object down toward the knife and slide the knife carrier toward the object until it is seen by close inspection that the further lowering of the object will just barely miss the knife. Then tighten the knife-carrier clamps.

Set the cam to cut sections of the desired thickness; 10 microns is standard for routine work. Now turn the wheel and make a number of revolutions rapidly until the paraffin block is contacted and begins to be sliced. Make sure that the bottom edge of the block, the one that the knife enters, is exactly aligned with the edge of the blade; this is necessary to make the sections *ribbon;* that is, to make each section, as cut, adhere to the preceding, forming a chain. While you are cutting paraffin alone, before the level of the tissue is reached, you can see whether the ribbon is forming properly and if not, make the necessary corrections of adjustments. If all is going well, cut the sections of tissue rapidly, using a camel's-hair brush held in the

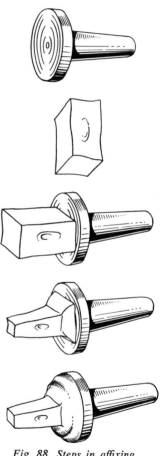

Fig. 88. Steps in affixing paraffin block to object carrier, trimming block, and building up paraffin shoulder.

left hand to pick up the end of the ribbon, support it, and carry it away from the instrument while the right hand does the cranking. When the ribbon attains a length of between 6 and 10 in., stop the cutting, pick up a second brush with the right hand, use it to lift the last-cut section from the blade, and with the two brushes deposit the length of ribbon on a sheet of stiff, glazed paper on the table at your left. A shallow but wide cardboard box lid forms a convenient tray for handling cut ribbons, the rim protecting them from drafts. When enough sections have been cut for the purpose at hand, if there is still some uncut tissue in the paraffin block, it may be cut from the carrier and stored, carefully labeled, for future use.

Nothing must touch the sectioned ribbons. Be careful of dust and drafts and do not breathe on them; they are so light that the slightest current of air will carry them away. Guard against the chance opening of a nearby door while you are cutting, and woe unto the microscopist who sneezes! Never touch the ribbon with the fingers, as the body heat will cause the paraffin to adhere. In handling ribbons, use the camel's-hair brush, or a forceps, toothpick, needle, or glass rod. Ribbons may be stored in boxes, but it is safest to get on with the processing if at all possible.

Here are some of the difficulties most commonly encountered in paraffin sectioning, with their causes and remedies.

1. Unless the top and bottom of the block are trimmed squarely with the plane of the edge of the knife, the ribbon will come away in a curve instead of a straight line. The two vertical sides of the block should also be trimmed square unless the nature of the material makes it important to be able to recognize top from bottom, as in cutting serial sections of an embryo; in such a case trim one side vertically, the other obliquely.

2. If the knife is dull, the sections may wrinkle or jam together, or they may refuse to ribbon, or each section as cut may cling to the block instead of to the knife. If, in such cases, a regulation microtome knife is being used, shift to a new region of the blade; if the whole edge turns out to be dull, a honing and stropping is in order. This is a tedious and lengthy process. The professional microtomist must learn how to do this properly, but others may well take advantage of the

sharpening service provided by supply houses, where most of the labor is performed by machines. If a safety-razor blade in a special holder designed for using these blades in microtomes is being employed, discard the blade and take a fresh one; Gillette makes a special superior blade for this purpose alone.

3. If the tissue is cooked by overheating in the paraffin, it will crumble or drop out of the ribbon or cause scratching noises in the cutting. There is of course no remedy for this defect; another piece of tissue will have to be processed. Should the knife ring or scrape in rising, the trouble may be that the object is too hard to cut in paraffin or too hard to cut with a thin blade, or the tilt of the knife may be too little or too great. Try first a change in tilt; then, failing correction, try a heavier knife, if available, or cut by another method.

4. A nick in the knife blade will cause scratches in the tissue or even split the ribbon. Shift the knife over to avoid the nick, or resharpen. Too soft a paraffin will result in jammed sections or sections that cling to the block. Reembed in a harder paraffin; or try chilling the block while cutting by suspending a tray of ice cubes over the instrument; or try cutting at 20 microns. The electrical conditions of the atmosphere may be wrong, causing sections to curl or cling to the side of the knife; wait until conditions change, or boil some water near the microtome so that the air becomes more humid.

5. Crystals of fixer carried over, alcohol or xylene·still present, may ruin results. Do not let paraffin accumulate on the knife blade; carefully wipe the blade upward, toward the edge, from time to time with a soft cloth moistened in xylene. If the machine cuts first a thin section, then a thick one, or misses every other section, the tilt may be wrong, the blade too thin, the object too tough, or some of the clamps not securely tightened. Old machines with worn parts may show this defect.

6. There are many troubles that may arise, but probably the most frequent and annoying one is having the sections roll and refuse to ribbon. This may be caused by any of numerous conditions, which will have to be tested one at a time. The knife may be dull, the tilt may be wrong, or the paraffin may be too hard. It is suggested that the following remedies be tried, in order: change the blade or the region of the knife being used for cutting; change the tilt; breathe on the knife

before each of several successive cuts, endeavoring to get a ribbon started, then cut rapidly; bring a lamp near the microtome to warm it; cut sections thinner; hold down a curled section with a brush and in that way try to get a ribbon started. Experience is the only teacher in microtoming. Normally the work will progress satisfactorily if the operator has seen to the basic requirements.

Affixing Sections. Using a scalpel, sharp knife, or safety-razor blade, cut the paraffin ribbon into portions suited for mounting. If the plant stem is of sizeable diameter, then one section to a slide is sufficient; if it is small, like clover, then it is customary to mount two or three per slide. Prepare a number of clean slides and lay them out on a paper on the table before you. Touch one small drop of Mayer's albumen affixative (page 166), as delivered by a glass applicator rod or a toothpick, to each slide, and with a clean fingertip spread this droplet evenly over the whole slide except the left end, which is reserved for the label. Wipe off in this manner all observable affixative; the exceedingly thin film that remains will do the trick and will not interfere with later observations under the microscope.

Now flood each slide with water and transfer the portion of ribbon allocated for each to its slide, centering the portions. Then, one slide at a time, warm gently over a low flame (preferably from an alcohol lamp); heat for a moment, withdraw, heat again, withdraw, etc., taking care not to melt the paraffin at any time. The object is to cause the ribbon to flatten out; this is called *spreading* the ribbon. It should become smooth and flat, with all wrinkles ironed out, and will increase in area about 20 per cent; allowance must be made for this expansion whenever serial sections, which fill a slide, are being spread. As the water evaporates the section is drawn down ever more closely into the albumen, and soon the section will be attached, to the extent that the remaining water may be drained off by tilting or by the application of a bit of torn edge of paper toweling to one side of the paraffin square. Then the slide is stored for twenty-four hours to dry thoroughly before the next step.

To repeat: warm slowly and gently, seeing to it that the paraffin does not melt. It becomes more translucent and perfectly smooth and flat. While the section is still afloat, adjust its position; poke it gently at the edge with a camel's-hair brush to keep it over the center of the slide. After it once starts to be affixed in the albumen, it is too late to alter the position.

There are alternative methods that many workers prefer. The ribbons may be floated and spread in a crystallizing dish of warm (not hot!) water, and the sections then cut apart with scissors. An albumenized slide is brought up under such a floating section, and the remainder of the centering and drying carried out as just described. Some add 3 per cent formalin to the water, which promotes affixing. An enameled pie tin is a good substitute utensil for this work. The professional laboratory goes at the same task in still another way, using an *electric slide dryer*, or *warming plate*, or *spreading plate*, as variously termed. A homemade model is not at all difficult to construct. Build a box of sheet asbestos or Sheetrock, about the size of a shoebox; use a copper plate for the top and allow one end of this plate to project beyond one end of the box by some 4 in.; i.e., if the box measures 5 by 10 in., the copper plate should be 5 by 14 and should project at one end only. The inside is wired for an electric bulb, near the bottom of the end opposite that where the top projects, and some ventilating holes are made along the sides. Use a 40-watt bulb and place the slides along the copper plate, each with the tissue floating on a film of water. By trial, that place is found where heat will hasten evaporation but not melt the paraffin. Directly over the bulb will probably prove too hot; farther along, the safe zone will begin, and slides may be placed from that point on out.

Staining. Slides with affixed tissues may be stored indefinitely; once dry they are permanently preserved, and we have known of sections stained twenty years after cutting that came out as well as though done the day after. But once the following steps are begun they must be carried through without interruption; it is therefore important that the technician map out a schedule and not begin the sequence until he is sure that it can be completed without interference.

The preferred glassware item for this work is the *Coplin jar* (Fig. 89). It has slots to receive slides, so that a number may be carried through simultaneously. By placing slides in pairs, back-to-back, the complement may be doubled. But even if

Fig. 89. Coplin staining jar.

only one slide is to be stained at a time, this jar is still the best type to use, as the slide is supported in a vertical position in the center of the jar and is most readily grasped and transferred. When changing a slide from one Coplin jar to the next, lift the slide out of the fluid except for one corner; this is held against the lip of the jar at an angle to drain for an instant, so as not to carry over more than is necessary of the contents of one jar to that of the next. For this reason some workers wipe the back of the slide and the front beyond the tissue against a towel. Care must of course be exercised not to wipe off the tissue inadvertently. Hold a slide and look along its surface at an oblique angle to determine on which side the tissue lies. Do the transferring rapidly so that the tissue at no time has an opportunity to become dry. Keep the lids on the jars at all times except when actually transferring slides; grease the lid of the 100A jar. Ten Coplin jars will be needed for the present technique.

The first two jars are labeled xylene 1 and xylene 2. Take up a slide with its affixed paraffin section and warm it gently over a low flame, constantly removing and reinserting it in the flame, so as to melt the paraffin but not cook the tissue; the object is to render the paraffin more quickly soluble in the xylene. Place it in the jar marked xylene 1 for ten minutes, then in xylene 2 for the same time. Jar 1 removes most of the paraffin, and jar 2 is supposed to get rid of the remainder. After some ten slides have been processed in this way, advance jar 2 to the position of jar 1, discard the xylene of No. 1, and refill with fresh xylene, starting it again as jar 2. If paraffin is carried over into the alcohols, it will interfere with subsequent staining.

Now pass down the *alcohol ladder*—that is, go through a series of Coplin jars labeled 100A, 95A, 82A, 70A, and 50A, and a final one of tap water. This is *hydrating*, i.e., adding water by successive steps. Going up the ladder is *dehydrating*, i.e., removing water in stages. One minute in each jar is sufficient, then change the slide to safranin for twenty-four hours. The preferred form of this dye is safranin O, but others are acceptable for general work, and the preferred strength is a saturated aqueous solution. Another formula liked by many is Babe's fluid, a mixture of equal parts of a saturated aqueous and a saturated alcoholic (95A) solution. This is a powerful and brilliant red dye, but it is extracted rapidly during the dehydrating and counterstaining procedures; hence the tissue must be intensely stained to begin with, and the time allowed for the follow-up steps must be cut to a minimum. Wash out according to the vehicle used for the stain; in tap water if an aqueous solution was used, in 50A if Babe's fluid was used.

Dehydrate rapidly, leaving the slide for 30 seconds in each jar in going up the ladder to 95A; then with the slide resting face up across a Syracuse watch glass, drop on the counterstain, fast green FCF for 30 seconds. This stain should be a 0.5 per cent solution in 95A. It may be placed in a Coplin jar and the slide immersed, but we prefer to use a *dropping bottle* (Fig. 90). Apply 1 to 2 drops of the stain, keeping the tissue covered with it, then drain quickly into the watch glass, and immediately put the slide into the 95A to rinse, then into 100A for one minute and xylene for ten minutes. This xylene must be in a jar other than the two used in deparaffining, as it must not contain any trace of paraffin. The slide should remain in xylene until the tissue is *clear*, i.e., completely translucent. It may take more or less time than the specified ten minutes. Then complete the slide with a mountant and cover glass. A finished cross section of a plant stem is shown in Figure 91.

Fig. 90. Dropping bottle.

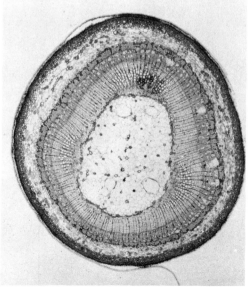

Fig. 91. Stained section of one-year-old basswood stem, 50×.

A ZOOLOGICAL SLIDE   Any one of a great many kinds of animals may be used as the source of a subject. Frog and rat are favorites, but perhaps parts of the cat have been put onto more tens of thousands of slides than those of any other species. We may select any organ as our first example. One of the most instructive is the intestine, so we shall choose cat intestine as our material, though these directions may be used equally well with a great variety of other preparations.

Chloroform or ether (caution! explosive when mixed with air!) may be employed, but for a mammal such as the cat, the best killing agent is illuminating gas. A rectangular box of suitable size may be made into a lethal chamber by boring a hole near one corner to admit a brass or rubber tube connected to a gas outlet. If not much of this work is to be done, it may be preferable occasionally to obtain a freshly killed animal from the city pound or humane society. Also, it should be possible to obtain small bits of pig or cow tissue from the local abattoir.

As a fixer we shall try the popular Bouin's fluid, one of a number that could be used. This is a picro-acetic-formalin, employed in general histologic work. One first makes a saturated aqueous solution of picric acid; 1 gm. of the yellow crystals will saturate about 75 cc. of water. Then to 75 cc. of this solution add 25 cc. commercial formalin and 5 cc. glacial acetic acid. With a quantity of Bouin's fluid at hand, remove a portion of cat intestine about ½ in. long, making two cuts with a sharp scalpel and handling the piece with forceps. Rinse the piece quickly in normal saline solution to remove food, blood, and hair and place it in an amount of Bouin's fluid roughly equal to 100 times the volume of the piece of intestine. Fix for overnight or allow it to remain until you are ready to continue; you cannot overfix with Bouin's.

Wash in two or more changes of 50A solution for two hours, then leave it in 70A for one to two days, with several changes, or until the alcohol ceases to extract the yellow color of the fixer. To the last 70A add enough lithium carbonate to saturate the solution, as this helps decolorize, then complete the dehydration and go on to paraffin embedding, sectioning, and affixing sections to slides as directed for the plant-stem material.

190

Remove the paraffin with two jars of xylene, run the slides down the alcohol ladder, and stain in Delafield's hematoxylin for thirty minutes. This solution may be made from crystals, but it requires aging and is somewhat more difficult to prepare than the average dye, so the user of small quantities will probably find it advantageous to buy the solution ready for use. After staining, wash in tap water for five minutes with frequent gentle agitation of the slide. This will help remove excess stain; the tissue should appear blue. Now pass the slide into 35 per cent acid alcohol (from a few seconds to a few minutes), until the section appears reddish, then into 35 per cent alkaline alcohol until the blue color is restored. This procedure sharpens the stain in the nuclei of the cells and prevents the carrying over of excess acid. The alkaline alcohol is prepared by making a 0.1 per cent solution of bicarbonate of soda in distilled water. Add only 3 to 5 drops of this weak solution to the 35A rinse. Larger amounts of salt are likely to make the tissues muddy; indeed, you may find by trial that your local tap water is sufficiently alkaline, in which case the 35A may be made up with this water; if it blues the slides then it is satisfactory.

Go up the ladder with one minute each in 50A, 70A, 82A, and then into eosin, the counterstain. This dye should bear the label "Eosin Y, water- and alcohol-soluble." The Y indicates "yellowish," the other kind being "bluish." It may be made up in water or alcohol of any strength; different technicians have different preferences. In the present example, make a 0.5 per cent solution in 95A and apply it with a dropping bottle pipette for from thirty seconds to one minute. A rapid inspection, keeping the tissue wet with 95A, will show when the red is sufficiently intense. Rinse in 95A to check the counterstaining, go through 100A to xylene, and mount. The completed preparation is shown in Figure 92.

Other subjects

In botany, the principal plant parts to section are root, stem, leaf, flower, and fruit. Among favorite slide preparations are pine root, stem, needles (leaves), and young cones, both staminate and pistillate; corn stem, germinating seed; lily flower bud; iris leaf; basswood stem; buttercup root, stem; lilac leaf.

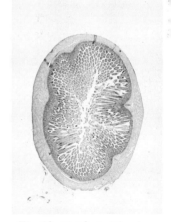

Fig. 92. Finished slide of cross section of cat intestine.

In the animal kingdom, cross sections are made of the little fresh-water polyp, hydra; of the small fresh-water flatworm, planaria; of the earthworm. In vertebrate histology, all the organs of the body are sectioned, the principal ones being brain (cerebrum, cerebellum, medulla), spinal cord; a skeletal muscle, such as the biceps; skin and scalp; esophagus, stomach, small intestine, large intestine, liver, and pancreas; trachea and lung; kidney and urinary bladder; ovary and testis; heart, large artery and vein, spleen; pituitary, thyroid, and adrenal glands. Bone and tooth, as well as nut shells and fruit pits, are ground down on an emery wheel, in much the same way that rock sections are prepared. There are endless special slides and also certain difficult subjects, such as eye and ear, that are beyond the scope of introductory work.

Other fixers

Rivals to F.A.A. for the favor of botanists are fixers based on chromic acid. Those containing 1 cc. chromic, 5 cc. glacial acetic acid, and 100 cc. water, or similar proportions, are called *chromacetic* fixers and are very good. But still better for most purposes are the ones in which formalin is added. The chrom-acetic-formal mixtures have been dubbed the *craf* fixers. The stock solution of a typical formula is 80 cc. of a 1 per cent solution of chromic acid in distilled water plus 5 cc. glacial acetic acid. Just before using, add half as much commercial formalin as stock; i.e., if about 100 cc. is the amount of fixer judged suitable for the purpose at hand, mix 66 cc. stock and 33 cc. formalin.

Fix for six to twelve hours, then wash in running water, six hours in the dark, to prevent precipitation; continue the dehydrating also in the dark. A simple apparatus for washing in running water is shown in Figure 93, using just a bare trickle from the faucet.

Three very excellent fixers employ bichloride of mercury as the principal ingredient. Recall the precautions in the use of this very poisonous material and its corrosive action on all metals (page 167), as well as the necessity for adding iodine solution to the 70A in dehydration to remove mercury "pins." Put in enough iodine to give the alcohol a port-wine color and

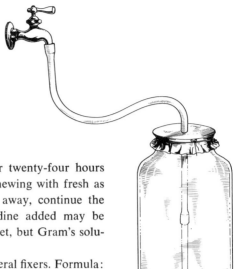

Fig. 93. Setup for washing tissues in running water.

add more if this color is extracted. After twenty-four hours change to 82A to wash out the iodine, renewing with fresh as needed, and when no more color comes away, continue the dehydrating by going into 95A. The iodine added may be tincture of iodine from the medicine cabinet, but Gram's solution (page 167) is better.

Gilson's fluid is one of the best of all general fixers. Formula: mercuric chloride, 5 gm., 80 per cent nitric acid, 4 cc., glacial acetic acid, 1 cc., 95A, 15 cc., distilled water, 220 cc. After the mixture has stood for three days, filter and bottle it. Fix small and delicate objects thirty minutes, medium ones two hours, large and dense ones six hours. In washing, go direct from fixer into 70 per cent iodinized alcohol.

Zenker's fluid consists of 2.5 gm. potassium bichromate, 5 gm. mercuric chloride, 1 gm. sodium sulfate, and 100 cc. distilled water. When bottled, this should be labeled "Zenker stock." Below this paste another label, reading: "To use, add 5 per cent glacial acetic acid." If the acetic is added earlier, the mixture deteriorates. Fix for overnight and up to twenty-four hours for dense material. However, do not overfix, which is easy to do in any mixture containing mercuric chloride; when the object is completely opaque, it is fixed and should be removed. Wash it in running water for the same number of hours used in fixing. Zenker's is probably the most widely used of the older fixers; fixation is unexcelled, and any stain may follow.

Helly's fluid is a formalin Zenker's fluid, preferred by many. Use the Zenker stock, but instead of adding acetic acid substitute formalin (full-strength) in the same amount and manner. Time and washing are the same as with Zenker's solution.

The number of biological dyes and combinations of them is legion, and we can refer here to but a few. Already described are borax carmine for the bee sting (page 155), Wright's stain for blood (page 158), crystal violet in the section on bacteriology (page 165), and fast green for protozoa (page 167).

Acid fuchsin is generally made as a 0.5 per cent aqueous solution. It is a very fine red cytoplasmic stain and should not be confused with basic fuchsin.

Van Gieson's picrofuchsin stains nuclei and epitheliums brown, white fibrous connective tissue red, and elastic and muscle tissue yellow. Such slides look quite different from the customary hematoxylin and eosin preparations and are very attractive. To make them, take one part of a 1 per cent aqueous solution of acid fuchsin to ten parts of a saturated aqueous solution of picric acid. Use as a counterstain after hematoxylin. Overstain with hematoxylin, rinse in water, and counterstain for five minutes in picrofuchsin. Add a pinch of picric acid crystals to each of the alcohols used in dehydration and to the xylene. This is a particularly good stain for sections of organs containing an abundance of connective tissue.

Ehrlich's acid hematoxylin is preferred to Delafield's stain by many. It gives a reddish rather than a bluish tint but, even so, contrasts well with eosin.

Other techniques

Cellosolve is the trade name of an industrial solvent, ethylene glycol monoethyl ether, that has met with favor as a substitute for alcohol in microtechnique. After tissue is fixed and washed, it is blotted with paper toweling and placed in this reagent; if washing in water is omitted, as in the Bouin's fluid program, go direct from fixer into Cellosolve. Prepare two jars, labeled Cellosolve 1 and Cellosolve 2. The tissue is kept from one to two hours in each, though a longer stay does no harm. Go through two changes of xylene and thence to paraffin embedding, sectioning, affixing of sections to slides, and deparaffining, as we have done earlier in this chapter. From xylene go through two jars of Cellosolve, five minutes each, distilled water, stain, rinse, destain, rinse, then two jars of Cellosolve (they may be the same as in descending the ladder), counterstain, with the dye dissolved in Cellosolve instead of in alcohol, clear, and mount.

Dioxan is another industrial solvent that is employed in the same manner. Owing to its poisonous properties, we do not recommend it for use by those whose work is unsupervised by a professional.

Hance's Embedding Mixtures. It is now possible to buy commercially some of the additions to paraffin for embedding that were introduced by Hance. He experimented with chopping up crude rubber, which is cooked up with paraffin, and then with the addition of beeswax, lanolin, and other additives that were designed to lower the melting point of the final wax so as to protect the tissues from the effects of heat, to prevent crystallizing, aid penetration, prevent excess hardening, and present a smooth-cutting, cohesive material. Hance's rubber-paraffin-beeswax mixture is recommended as decidedly superior to paraffin alone.

Repeated use of reagents

Fixing solutions and the paraffins are never used more than once. They should be discarded with due regard to possible damage to plumbing. Never pour melted paraffin into a sink; let it solidify, then put it with solid wastes.

Other reagents are used repeatedly until they show signs of wearing out and are then discarded. Whenever a tissue or slide is transferred from one vessel to another, it carries over into No. 2 some of the substance of No. 1, and thus the second is gradually adulterated. A stain becomes diluted with water, a higher alcohol weakened by a lower, and xylene polluted with either alcohol on the one hand or paraffin on the other, until it is unfit for further use. It is especially important that the xylene and 100A be reasonably pure.

Whenever it is desired to bottle a used reagent for storage, make certain that it is labeled as used. Never pour a used stain back into the stock bottle of unused stain, for example. Save the used higher alcohols (82, 95, and 100 mixed together) for cleaning glassware and tables.

Reversibility of procedures

It is fortunate that many of the steps in microtechnique are reversible. As noted earlier, tissues may be reembedded in paraffin if faults develop. In staining, should the affixed section turn out to be insufficiently colored, it may be restained, even when finished as a balsam mount, or incomplete dehydration or clearing may be corrected. Simply go backward in the sequence from the point where the imperfection is first noticed to the place where the correction is to be made, then forward again.

References

Corrington, J. D., *Working with the Microscope*, McGraw-Hill Book Company, Inc., New York, 1941.

Gray, P., *Handbook of Basic Microtechnique,* The Blakiston Division, McGraw-Hill Book Company, Inc., New York, 1952.

Gray, P., *The Microtomist's Formulary and Guide,* The Blakiston Division, McGraw-Hill Book Company, Inc., New York, 1954.

Guyer, M. F., *Animal Micrology,* 4th ed., University of Chicago Press, Chicago, 1936.

Lee, A. B., in Gatenby, J. B., and T. S. Painter, *The Microtomist's Vade-Mecum,* 10th ed., The Blakiston Division, McGraw-Hill Book Company, Inc., New York, 1937.

Sources for stains

In addition to those firms listed at the ends of Chapters 4 and 5, there are the following special sources for biological dyes and microtechnical reagents:

J. T. Baker Chemical Co., Phillipsburg, N.J. *Baker Analyzed* stains.

Hartman-Leddon Co., Inc., 5821 Market St., Philadelphia 39. *Harleco* reagents and Parstains.

Matheson Coleman & Bell, Inc., East Rutherford, N.J., or Norwood (Cincinnati), Ohio.

National Aniline Division, Allied Chemical & Dye Corporation, 40 Rector St., New York 6.

chapter thirteen

Adventuring with Sherlock Holmes

Sherlock Holmes had been bending for a long time over a low-power microscope. Now he straightened himself up and looked round at me in triumph.

"It is glue, Watson," said he. "Unquestionably it is glue. Have a look at these scattered objects in the field!" [Fig. 94].

I stooped to the eyepiece and focused for my vision.

"Those hairs are threads from a tweed coat. The irregular gray masses are dust. There are epithelial scales on the left. Those brown blobs in the centre are undoubtedly glue."

"Well," I said, laughing, "I am prepared to take your word for it. Does anything depend upon it?"

"It is a very fine demonstration," he answered. "In the St. Pancras case you may remember that a cap was found beside the dead policeman. The accused man denies that it is his. But he is a picture-frame maker who habitually handles glue."

"Is it one of your cases?"

"No; my friend Merivale, of the Yard, asked me to look into the case. Since I ran down that coiner by the zinc and copper filings in the seam of his cuff they have begun to realize the importance of the microscope." (Emphasis ours.)

— THE ADVENTURE OF SHOSCOMBE OLD PLACE *

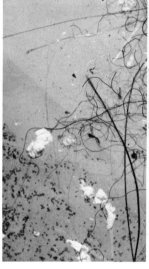

Fig. 94. Evidential slide in St. Pancras police murder. Tweed fibers at right, with particles of lint and dirt; epithelial scales on left; large whitish masses are glue. 11×.

Thus was announced to the vast reading public to whom the famous fictional detective was more of a reality than many a living person, the advent of science in the field of criminology.

* By permission of the Estate of Sir Arthur Conan Doyle, © 1927.

Yes, Watson, look well into that "low-power microscope" (the only one mentioned in all the chronicles of the Master), for you are looking at the birth of a new science. This portentous event occurred in the closing years of the nineteenth century and in the penultimate of all those wonderful adventures of the celebrated Baker Street pair. In that era we had also begun to read of Bertillon's measurements and descriptions of human physical features and Galton's work with fingerprints, but until the microscope was brought to bear upon a multitude of subjects that could be produced in courts as evidence, there was no organized body of knowledge concerning scientific criminal detection.

Today there are many laboratories—city, county, and Federal—throughout the land that are devoted to this work. Sometimes university specialists are called upon to contribute along the line of their special proficiency. A well-equipped police laboratory is provided with as many scientific instruments as the average hospital. Here are the chief departments into which the various investigations logically fall.

Personal identification

The need for a system that makes it possible to trace and identify individuals looms above all other aspects of crime detection. As everyone knows, fingerprinting is by no means confined to the records of those who are antisocial in their behavior; quite the contrary, since members of the armed forces in many countries, bank employees, and the gangs of illiterate laborers who cannot sign a payroll are commonly fingerprinted. In fact, it was the plight of this last-named group that led Sir E. R. Henry, then inspector-general of police in the lower provinces in India, to elaborate on a system first proposed by the British scientist, Sir Francis Galton, and advanced by another equally celebrated compatriot, Sir William Herschel, the result being the famous Henry system of fingerprint classification. With modifications, Henry's plans survive today in all countries. Everyone should have his fingerprints on file with the FBI in Washington, for who knows when he will suddenly be the victim in a plane crash or an automobile collision? And who can anticipate amnesia? The occasions are many when, for the sake of those left behind and notably for the settlement of wills and insurance policies, it is of vital importance to establish the identity of the noncriminal deceased or amnestic.

But if fingerprints are of value to the law-abiding citizen, how much more important they are in establishing the identity of the criminal. Fingerprints are not concealed by aliases or disguises. Significant indeed is the fact that in the enormous files of the FBI in Washington, with hundreds of thousands of cards, better than 48 per cent, or practically half of all the cards received, are from persons with a previous record of crime!

If we look at one of our fingertips with a hand lens we shall find an alternation of ridges and depressions, like a distant view of a plowed field. The pores of sweat glands open along the ridges and are separately visible under high magnification. There are so many individual complexities that the probability of identical patterns being presented by two different fingerprints is only one in several millions of chances. When the complete set of ten fingers is considered, the likelihood of a duplicate set appearing in a second person has been estimated to occur only once in 10,000 years. If we add to such distinctiveness the very detailed and intricate arrangement of the openings of the sweat glands along the ridges, thousands of them in a single picture, it becomes obvious that not twice in the entire history of man on this planet has a single human fingerprint, much less a complete set of the ten digits of an individual, ever been duplicated in every minute respect.

The fingerprint record is maintained on stiff white cards (Figs. 95, 96) adapted for filing. In making the prints one needs a metal, marble, or plate-glass slab on which black printer's ink is smeared to a thin film with a hard-rubber roller. Separate *rolled prints* are first made of each finger, placed on the card in the square designated for the particular digit. If you are interested in this work and wish to make prints, have your own made first at your local police headquarters or county sheriff's office, and observe closely how it is done. You can "roll your own," but it is better to have someone do it for you.

The operator grasps your right thumb with the thumb and first fingers of both of his own hands and applies its left mar-

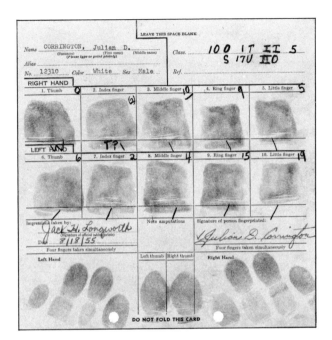

Fig. 95. Reverse of Finger-print Record Card.

gin, terminal joint, to the inked slab. He rolls it over on the slab with moderate speed and pressure, then immediately carries the thumb across to the card and repeats the action, applying the thumb to square No. 1 and rolling it over as before, from left to right, with the same speed and pressure, then lifts it clear. This action spreads the print out to approximately twice the width of a stamped print, making the pattern much easier to read. This procedure is repeated for each of the ten digits, the only variation being that those of the left hand are rolled in the opposite direction, from right to left.

Then the inked slab is rolled to eradicate the impressions previously made in the inked film, and the two thumbs, side by side, are placed on the slab, the action being that of stamping, as in using a stamp pad, then transferred without altering their position, to the bottom center of the card, where *stamped prints* (plain prints) are impressed. Similarly, the four remaining digits of first the left hand then the right are inked and

CRIMINAL BUREAU OF INVESTIGATION, DADE COUNTY SHERIFF'S OFFICE

MIAMI, FLORIDA

(PLEASE PASTE PHOTO HERE)

Date of arrest ....
Charge ....
Disposition of case ....

Residence ....
Place of birth ....
Nationality ....
Occupation ....

F. B. I. NO.

Age .... Date of birth ....
Height .... Comp. .... Hair ....
Weight .... Eyes .... Build ....
Scars and marks ....

CRIMINAL HISTORY

NAME	NUMBER	CITY OR INSTITUTION	DATE	CHARGE	DISPOSITION OR SENTENCE

ACCOMPLICES

NAME	NUMBER	NAME	NUMBER	NAME	NUMBER

FORM 2-99

Fig. 96. Obverse of Fingerprint Record Card.

stamped, the fingers flat and close together. This second set of prints is to serve as a check on the first in case any digit has been applied out of its proper sequence through inadvertence. In a case of law infringement, the operator and culprit each sign the card, and data as to the charge, vital statistics, history, and accomplices are added on the other side; then the record is ready for coding.

In the Henry system, with certain present-day modifications, the prints are referable to three main types—arches, loops, and whorls—each with subdivisions. In the *arch* type of print (Fig. 97) the friction ridges pass across from one side to the other, gradually rising in the center of the impression until the central ridges are arched to a considerable degree. None of the ridges makes a backward turn. If one of them has a sharp upward turn and forms a central axis in a vertical plane, the print is termed a *tented arch* and designated on the card record with T (Fig. 95, digit 2, questioned as to whether

Fig. 97. An arch. (Courtesy Bausch & Lomb.)

Fig. 98. A loop. (Courtesy Bausch & Lomb.)

Fig. 99. A whorl. (Courtesy Bausch & Lomb.)

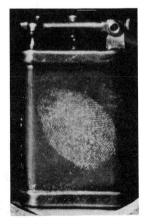

Fig. 100. A dusted fingerprint on a cigarette lighter.

tented arch or loop). A doubtful print is cross-referenced under both categories.

Some of the ridges in the *loop* type make a backward turn but do not form complete circles (Fig. 98). If the downward direction of the general slope of the loop is toward the little finger, the loop is termed *ulnar* and designated U, the ulna being the bone of the forearm on that side of the hand; if the direction is toward the thumb side, the loop is *radial* (R), the radius being the bone on the thumb side of the forearm. On the card record (Fig. 95), loops are indicated by oblique lines—/—the slope of the line showing whether it is ulnar or radial. In this particular record, all digits except 1 and possibly 2 are loops, and all are ulnar.

Whorls (Fig. 99) include ridges that make complete circles and spirals and are either single-cored or double-cored; digit 1 of Figure 95 is a double-cored whorl; Figure 99 is single-cored.

In police practice all objects about the vicinity of a crime are carefully inspected through reading glasses for any evidence of fingerprints, and all items presumably handled by persons connected with the events are automatically dusted with powder to see what may be found. Any smooth surface (Fig. 100)—furniture, glass, metal—will retain a print admirably, whereas prints upon rough surfaces are usually so fragmentary and broken as to be worthless. A good print, even though of a single fingertip, or a mere portion of one impression, is valuable and is prepared for photographing by dusting with fine powder. On paper, *latent fingerprints* (those needing treatment to become visible) are developed by chemicals, while dusted prints may be *lifted* by the application of an adhesive tape. Prints may be impressions made by the natural oil and perspiration of the skin, or they may be produced by some liquid in which the fingers have been immersed or in contact, e.g., they may be outlined in blood.

Wearing gloves to thwart this system is not so prevalent among criminals as one is led to believe from detective fiction. Many crimes, notably homicide, are committed in the heat of passion or without deliberation and so without preparation; some offenders are ignorant, some careless, and in still other cases gloves hamper operations, as in opening safes. Burglars sometimes begin work with gloves only to discard them later in impatience at their restrictions. Cases are on record of good prints obtained through a hole in the fingertip of a glove, or through gloves of extreme thinness.

The fingerprint pattern is present at birth and remains unaltered throughout the life of the individual. A set of impressions made from an infant is identical, except in size, with a set from the same person in old age. Prints may be obtained from dead and even from embalmed bodies, in fact at any time until destruction of the tissues results from decay. Attempts to mutilate the pattern are usually of no avail, since when new skin is regenerated the same pattern reappears, and scars either do not sufficiently efface the old print or are themselves highly distinctive when subjected to microscopic examination.

Unquestionably fingerprints constitute by far the most positive and reliable method for the identification of human individuals yet discovered. The prints themselves, the microscope, and the system of classification are among the most powerful of all weapons that organized society has at its disposal in dealing with antisocial persons. For presentation as evidence in court, there is one other important ally—the *comparison microscope* (Fig. 101). This ingenious instrument

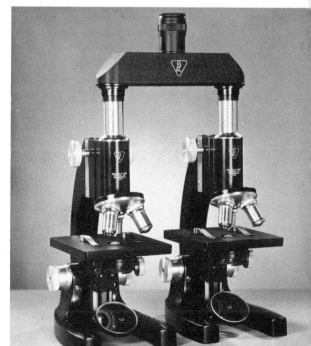

Fig. 101. A comparison microscope made by attaching the comparison eyepiece to two identical monocular microscopes. (Courtesy Bausch & Lomb.)

permits comparison, side by side, of materials from two sources, enabling the observer to form an opinion as to whether they were originally from the same source. There are two objectives that scan two fields, which should be uniformly illuminated. At the top of the two tubes is a prism housing, so that the image-forming rays are directed to a composite real image scanned by a single eyepiece. This ocular has a hairline dividing it vertically into halves. The left half of the image seen comes from the left objective, and the right half from the right objective.

The comparison microscope has many uses, but we are concerned here with fingerprints. Two prints are to be checked as to their identity; one obtained from a suspect and the other from the scene of a crime in which he is alleged to have participated. A print is mounted under each objective and the two are moved so as to attempt to match up the two half-images. If the prints are identical, they can readily be matched across the hairline (Fig. 102), all ridges showing perfect continuity; this would clearly be impossible if the prints were from different fingers.

For purposes of a slide collection, fingerprints may be made directly on the glass slide, but they show to better advantage if they are on heavy white paper, the finished slide to be examined by incident light. All one needs, when the print is thoroughly dry, are mountant and cover glass. A set of different types adds a group of decidedly interesting mounts to the collection.

Fig. 102. Two halves of prints from same finger matched in a photograph through the comparison microscope. (Courtesy Bausch & Lomb.)

Forensic medicine

The title of this section describes the broad field of presentation of medical testimony in a court of law. Forensic medicine deals with such things as circumstances surrounding births, time and cause of death, opinions as to whether a specified weapon could or could not have caused certain described injuries and as to the probability or certainty that these injuries resulted in death of the deceased, evidence from autopsies, and questions regarding the sanity of persons involved in criminal investigations. Forensic medicine, also termed medical jurisprudence, is the science of applying medical knowledge to the purposes of legal investigation and to judicial proceedings.

That part of forensic medicine that involves microscopy requires not so much the use of new subjects as different approaches to and points of view about those already well known. Cytology, histology, and pathology are the main fields of research concerned. Tissues and organs of many sorts may need to be demonstrated, as well as the effects on them of poisons, burns, blows, and gunshot and knife wounds. The technician may be called upon to prepare sections and also blood slides, sperm smears, or a mount of epithelial cells removed from under the fingernails of a victim, whose defense by scratching was not adequate.

The student of normal histology learns of the development and adult structure of human hair, but he is interested only in the average or typical hair. In criminological work one must study many kinds of hairs, classify the several thousands of sorts of human hairs, using them as a means of personal identification (for which purpose they are second in importance only to fingerprints) tell whether a hair is dyed or has natural color, whether it was cut or torn from the head, and whether it came from a part of the body other than the head. All this involves a very considerable specialized study, extending to the hairs of animals other than man. There are a few experts who have made this branch of investigation their life work.

In previous adventures we have made blood slides and seen that hemin crystals constitute a positive test for blood. Now we should prepare some slides of hair. In gathering material, remove one hair from the head with scissors and cut it into ½-in. lengths so that a number of these pieces may be mounted on one slide, then obtain a second hair by plucking, so that the bulb at the root end is acquired. If this subject proves interesting after you have gotten into it a bit, collect examples of different types of human hair, such as from Caucasians, Mongolians, Negroes; blond, red, brunet, black, and white; natural-color and dyed; cranial, facial (beard), axillary, and pubic; male and female; infant, child, and adult from the same person (possible when mother has saved junior's locks in dated envelopes in attic trunks). Then for comparison secure some

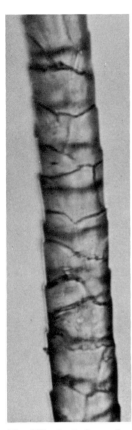

Fig. 103. Cuticular scales on surface of a bat hair, 741×.

hairs of common mammals, according to availability—dog, cat, rat, horse, cow, sheep, and pig, and from the various fur pieces present in the household, each of which, even the mutation mink, can stand the pilfering of a hair or two without damage. And make a special effort to obtain some bat hair (Fig. 103), which, for no apparent reason, is more elaborately sculptured than any other type and makes an especially attractive slide.

Several kinds of containers for hair specimens may be suggested—glassine envelopes are excellent, also pillboxes, matchboxes, and small vials; but perhaps best are gelatin capsules, veterinary size, obtainable in dozen lots at drug stores. Enclose short lengths of hairs in a capsule along with the data, written in ink with a fine pen on a tiny slip of onionskin paper.

The individual hairs, as obtained, will nearly always be too oily and too dusty to make first-class slide mounts. Clean the hairs by holding one or more with a forceps and waving them about in a mixture of equal parts of 95A and ether for a minute or two. Wash until they appear clean under the microscope. For temporary examination, as in identification, simply place a hair on a carefully cleaned slide and lay on a cover glass, without any mountant, then warm this slide gently over an alcohol lamp or on a slide dryer. For a permanent mount, remove the cover when the hair is perfectly dry, add mountant, and cover again.

The cuticular scales on the surface of a hair are best brought out by depositing pigment in them by staining. Iodine and methyl green have been used, but greatest success will be attained by employing a saturated solution of safranin in 95A. Immerse hairs in this stain for one or two minutes, remove the hairs and hold them in a draft of warm air, e.g., above a slide dryer, incubator, or electric bulb, until thoroughly dry, then mount in a thick mountant. If the mounting medium is too thin the safranin will come away from the hair and stain all the mountant.

The shaft of a hair is either circular in cross section (in Mongolians), elliptical (in Caucasians), or flattened (in Negroes), resulting, respectively, in perfectly straight hair, in wavy or curly hair, and in kinky or woolly hair. The detailed histology of hair need not detain us here, but there are four important structural features that should be studied under the microscope.

First comes the *cuticle*, a very thin and transparent outer layer composed of minute *scales* (Fig. 103). The scales may be *imbricate*, i.e., shingled and overlapping like the scales of a fish, or *coronal*, i.e., encircling the shaft as a continuous band; both these types have a number of subdivisions. Second, beneath the cuticle, comes the *cortex* of the hair shaft, composed of spindle-shaped cells so compacted that this layer generally appears transparent and uniform, with little structural distinctness. Keratin, or horn, similar to that in our fingernails, is deposited in the cortex, brings about the death of the cells, and imparts to the hair its characteristic cornified (horny) texture.

In some cases the color of a hair is due to material uniformly diffused throughout the cortex, but in most mammals it is produced by definite *pigment granules*, and the number and pattern of distribution of these granules are taken into account in identifying species. The fourth feature is the innermost layer of the hair shaft, the *medulla*, a column running the length of the shaft and containing shrunken cells, spaces, and dried and horny epidermal structures which present a picture characteristic of each species of mammal.

The cuticular scales are best brought out by safranin staining, the remaining features by unstained mounts; hence both stained and unstained portions should be mounted together. The most instructive portion of a hair is found about one-third of the distance from base to tip, starting from the base. Here the medulla reaches its greatest expansion and the cuticular scales are most highly developed. Farther out on the shaft the medulla is likely to be broken up and degenerate, and the scales are flatter and shorter.

Occupational and regional residues

A complete microscope slide library of reference in this division is hardly possible, for it would have to include samples of all the things with which people are in contact in their daily affairs. Specimen slides can be made up as required by specific cases, thus the accumulation of a huge collection, tying up time, space, and funds, is unnecessary. But the microscopist must have the proper background and training to be able to make and evaluate these slides. The making commonly involves no more than the application of xylene and mountant to perfectly dry subjects, but the evaluation will require wide knowledge and experience in science and industry, such as evidenced by Sherlock Holmes in the opening paragraphs of this chapter when he pointed out to Watson his determinations of hairs from a tweed coat, dust, epithelial scales, and glue.

Among materials that might be found on the person of a suspect or in his living quarters or place of work are wood residues (sawdust, splinters, shavings); smears or specks of paints and varnishes, dyes, and inks; metal residues (filings and turnings of iron, steel, copper, zinc, etc.); various dusts and powders (brick, cement, stone, flour, talc); sands and soils; textile and paper scraps, shreds, threads, lint; pollen grains, spores, seeds; food residues on clothing, and many others. Most readers will recall actual cases where materials of these sorts have figured importantly as evidence in trials.

The ways of the police in gathering such evidence are many and ingenious. An electromagnet will reclaim microscopic metal particles from a suit of clothes, even after the garments have been carefully brushed; fluorescent lamps will reveal substances not otherwise seen; X rays, ultraviolet, chemical developers—these and other methods of modern science are all at the disposal of experts in detection. A suspect claimed to have witnessed a will in 1925, but studies with the comparison microscope and fluorescent lighting showed that the ink with which he signed his name was of a sort unknown on the market before 1932, some years after the death of the person who supposedly executed the will.

We have already had some experience with residues. We have made and examined slides of textiles and paper and learned at least the rudiments of how to tell the different kinds of fibers one from another. We have made some slides of sands and soils and have studied methods of their formation and the subsequent shaping and sizing of their particles from weathering and erosion. Other excursions will follow along similar lines, requiring that we add continually to our fund of information about all the things around us.

An expert (and any person who applies himself can become

one) can identify the tree family and often the species of wood residues, depending on how much undestroyed material he has to work with. The safranin–fast green technique may be used on residues as well as on sections. Similarly, the different metals yield characteristic residues when filed, sawed, or drilled.

Here is a list of suggested mounts, needing only xylene and mountant, with or without cover-glass props or cell mounts, as the materials dictate: sample of contents of vacuum-cleaner bag [this should form an interesting puzzle slide, with lint (textile fibers), hairs from pet animals, and dust (mostly soil particles) predominating, but with here and there something unusual and unexpected]; filings of some common metals; sawdust and fine shavings and splinters from several common woods; tobacco residues that accumulate in pockets, pipe-tobacco pouches, and cigarette packs; fingernail filings, stained; silver and brass polish, diluted; toothpaste and powder, diluted; black pepper and kitchen spices; fur and hair of several animals, if not already mounted; cornstarch, talcum powder, and rouge; coal dust from the cellar; and don't forget some blobs of glue.

Ballistics

This science deals with projectiles, and that aspect having to do with criminology treats of ways and means of identifying guns and bullets, with a view to tracing the particular weapon used in a crime. Just as we have seen that fingerprints and sometimes hairs leave their telltale marks of individual identification, so too do rifles and pistols and their projectiles. If a firearm, other than the smooth-bored shotgun, is available, look down the barrel toward a light and observe the *rifling*, a system of spiral *grooves* cut into the bore of the barrel, leaving elevated areas, called *lands*, that cut into the surface of the bullet, producing *scratches*. The rifling gives the bullet a spiral twist as it leaves the gun, the principle being the same as in the feathering of an arrow; a rotary motion is imparted so that the projectile will fly true to its mark and not tumble end over end or drift sidewise.

No two bullets are marked precisely alike unless they have been discharged from the same gun. Even two weapons of the same make, model, and year will still show individual peculiarities in their rifling. For this reason the sheriff's office or the city police obtain a bullet, usually at autopsy, from the body of the person who has been shot, and holds it as an exhibit. Sooner or later they may arrest a suspect and find that he has a revolver in his possession. A bullet from this gun is fired into a bale of sphagnum moss or other substance from which it can be recovered undeformed. It is then placed in one of the chucks (holders) of a *bullet-comparison microscope* (Figs. 104, 105); the bullet from the victim's body is mounted in the other chuck. These two holders can be rotated so as to present the same face to the observer, and the two bullets are uniformly illuminated from a single fluorescent bulb. Each bullet is carefully focused. The single eyepiece of this instrument has a hairline dividing the two different images; the left half of the bullet on the left stage is aligned with the right half of the bullet on the right stage. If the two bullets have been fired from the same gun and have been marked identically, then their scratch pattern will match across the middle line (Fig. 106), whereas if they are from different sources their scratches will not match. The evidence presented by this ingenious machine can be recorded in the form of photomicrographs, which may be enlarged or projected for use in the courtroom.

Fig. 104. Bullet-comparison microscope, showing one eyepiece, two objectives, uniform lighting, two stands, each with mechanical stage; bullet shown mounted on chuck on left stage; mirror may be attached below (as on left stand) or above (right stand). (Courtesy Bausch & Lomb.)

Fig. 105. Inspector William A. Winfield, head of the Police Identification Bureau of Rochester, N. Y., adjusting chucks of bullet-comparison microscope. When setup is complete, microscope slides under camera for photographic recording of the evidence. (Courtesy Bausch & Lomb.)

This evidence is today admissible and has provided the clinching argument in many a case.

Scientific evidence of this sort is impersonal and impartial. The bullet-comparison microscope or any other of man's instrument assistants will testify for the innocent as well as for the guilty. When the bullet scratches will not match up across the dividing line, it is clear at least that the suspected gun was not the one involved in the crime; and this in turn may lead to setting the suspect free and clearing his name.

Another means of identification of a pistol are the *firing-pin marks* on the ejected cartridge cases. The criminal seldom has time to search for these cases and then to destroy them, and they will often prove whether or not the ejected shells were fired from the gun in question.

Questioned documents

Under this heading is classed an array of related topics having to do with forgeries, counterfeiting, check raising, sending poison-pen letters, making ransom demands, and other crimes involving writing in any of its several forms—handwriting,

Fig. 106. Photomicrograph of matched bullet scratches as seen through the bullet-comparison microscope. (Courtesy American Optical Co.)

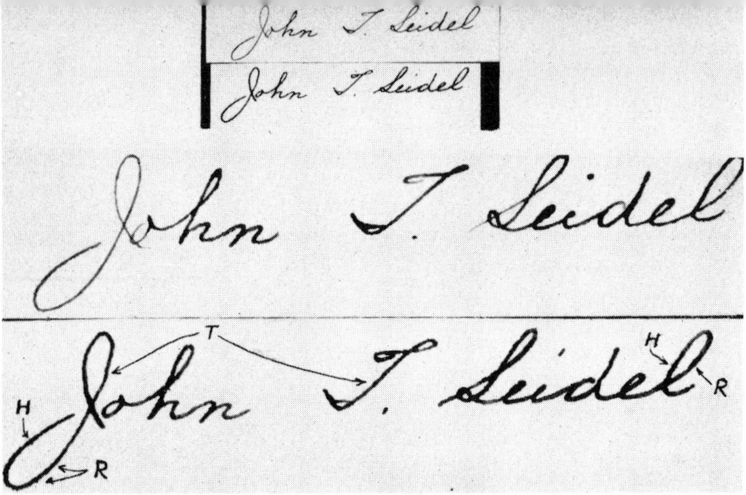

Fig. 107. *Forgery of a signature by tracing in upside-down position. Normal size; genuine above, forged below. Enlarged photographs; genuine above, forged below, show up the traced copy as spurious through hesitations (H), retracings (R), and tremor (T).*

typewriting, printing, engraving. The writing may be a forged signature to a will or a contract, a forged or raised check, or a letter making illegal demands or defamatory statements, and so it becomes the task of the scientific detective to prove whether the material is genuine or spurious.

There are experts who have made a lifetime study of *calligraphy*, or handwriting. Their testimony in court is given a weight proportional to their demonstrated or known wisdom and experience in this field, but it can never have the full force of the visual proof furnished by the microscope. If a forger takes the time to practice another man's writing until he can dash off a note or a signature freely and naturally, then the expert's opinion may be the only recourse open to law enforcement agencies, unless it can be shown that an unusual or unlikely ink or paper was employed, such as the rightful owner of the signature would never use.

But commonly a forgery is made by the *tracing* method, the crook having insufficient skill or time or patience to master another's writing. A genuine signature is obtained from a letter, a canceled check, a subscription to some fake enterprise, or in any of numerous other ways known to these people. A tracing box is contrived, with a glass top and a lamp below the glass; then the signature is placed on the glass, and the check, will, letter, or other document intended as a forgery is

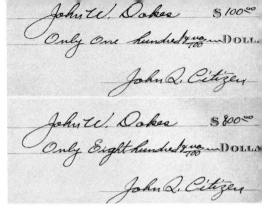

Fig. 108. Genuine check (above) and the same after raising the amount from $100 to $800.

placed over the signature at the proper position so that the signature shows through and may be copied by tracing. The criminal traces, believing this to be the one foolproof method to use. But he hasn't included the microscope in his reckonings. There will be evidence of *tremor*, since he is doing the tracing slowly, carefully, and not in a natural, rapid, easy-flowing style. Just as the lie detector shows unconscious tremor of muscles under certain tests, so will the traced signature exhibit the same involuntary, microscopic movements of the muscles involved. *Hesitation* will probably also be evident, when the pen stops for a fleeting moment at a place where it would not naturally stop in a genuine signature, and when more ink flows from the pen than ought to. Finally there will be *retracings*, where the forger lifts the pen, then puts it down again, never in the identical spot. Retracings are unnatural in a genuine signature. The traced name may appear authentic to the casual inspection of the unaided eye, but when it is magnified (Fig. 107), these three flaws stand out and proclaim the signature fraudulent.

Figures 108 and 109 show one of the several ingenious ways

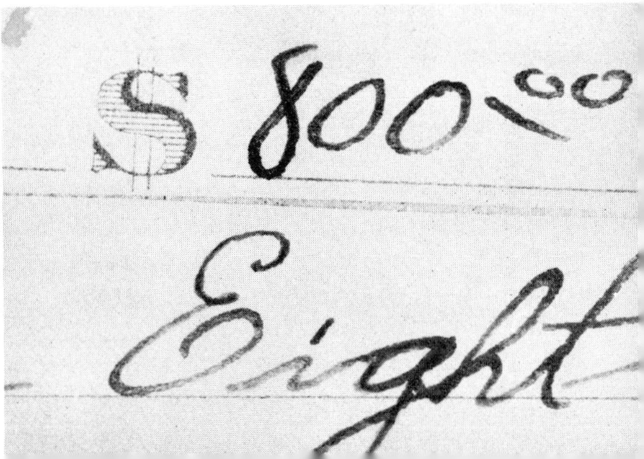

Fig. 109. Magnified view of portion of raised check, revealing its spurious nature.

213

in which a check can be raised, and the appearance of an alteration, with and without magnification. Not only will retracing show, but the exact color of ink and width and type of pen can be seen to vary, especially when examined under fluorescent light. And of course any *erasures*, no matter how skillfully done with either mechanical or chemical means, are certain to disturb the fibers of the paper surface. Such disturbance is easily seen when magnified. To make it more obvious, however, check and draft paper is now made so that the slightest attempt at erasure makes a glaring botch in the finish of the paper. Such paper and check writers that perforate the paper make the check raiser look elsewhere for a victim.

Counterfeiting has come in for attention in our discussion of paper (page 116), and so we shall turn to a final section on typewriting. Readers of detective fiction will anticipate what we shall say here, as this has been a favorite topic. Just as no two manufacturers of revolvers put exactly the same style of rifling in their gun barrels, so no two makers of typewriters have identical factory methods, and various machines are characteristic of their producers. In addition to different brands and models of machines, there are different sizes and styles of type faces, e.g., the regulation pica, the large, open gothic, the small elite, and the personal script. But, to narrow the field, let us now picture two typewriters of the same make and model and with the same type faces, going through the factory side by side, supposedly as alike as the two proverbial peas in a pod.

However, because the final adjustment and alignment of the type bars and spring tensions must be done by hand, the personal equation enters, and it is not possible for two typewriters to leave the factory so exactly alike in these respects that slight differences, detectable under magnification, cannot be found. The longer these machines are in use, the greater the discrepancies become (Fig. 110).

Let us say that the police are looking for the typewriter on which a ransom note was written so that they can narrow their inquiries to those having access to this machine. They will copy the text of the message on every typewriter owned or available to all suspects. If they succeed in finding the right one, they can make photomicrographic enlargements of portions of

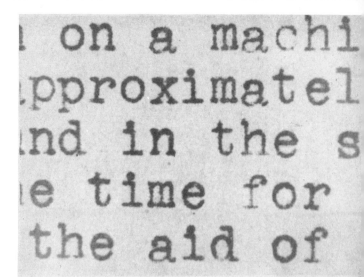

Fig. 110. Enlargement of portion of typewritten material. Among many small deviations, note that the "a" type bar strikes too far to the left and too low, and that the dot over the "i" is not separated from the stem of the letter.

the note typed on it to compare with a similar presentation of the same part of the ransom note. They will then point out to a jury the minute agreements: the letter "a" is out of alignment, printing a trifle too high, the "h" prints closer to the letter on its right than it should, the upper half of the "x" inks more heavily than the lower half, and so on. As the number of these small maladjustments increases, the probability that both notes were written on the same typewriter also increases; compounding such maladjustments soon makes the probability a certainty.

There is much more to scientific crime detection than can be included in a single chapter. Our aim has been to introduce you to the subject. If your interest has been aroused, we suggest that you make the acquaintance of your sheriff or your chief of police and ask to see some of their instruments and the ways in which they are used.

References

Dienstein, W., *Technics for the Crime Investigator,* Charles C Thomas, Publisher, Springfield, Ill., 1952.

Duncan, J. H., *Introduction to Fingerprints,* Butterworth & Co., (Publishers) Ltd., London, 1943.

Eiseman, J. S., *Elements of Investigative Techniques,* McKnight & McKnight Publishing Company, Bloomington, Ill., 1949.

Fitzgerald, M. J., *Handbook of Criminal Investigation,* Greenberg: Publisher, Inc., New York, 1951.

Fricke, C. W., *Criminal Investigation,* 5th ed., O. W. Smith, Los Angeles, 1949.

Gross, H. G. A., *Criminal Investigation,* 4th ed., Carswell, Toronto, 1950.

Hatcher, J. S., *Textbook of Firearms Investigation, Identification and Evidence* (and) *Textbook of Pistols and Revolvers,* Small-Arms Technical Publishing Co., Marines, Onslow County, N.C., 1936.

Kirk, P. L., *Crime Investigation,* Interscience Publishers, Inc., New York, 1953.

Kuhne, F., *The Finger Print Instructor,* Scientific American Publishing Co., New York, 1935.

Lucas, A., *Forensic Chemistry and Scientific Criminal Investigation,* 4th ed., Longmans, Green & Co., Inc., New York, 1946.

Osborn, A. S., *Questioned Documents,* Boyd Printing Co., Albany, N.Y., 1929. Out of print but often available from dealers.

Turner, R. F., *Forensic Science and Laboratory Technics,* Charles C Thomas, Publisher, Springfield, Ill., 1949.

Index

218

Butterfly wing scales, 150

228

About the Author

Julian D. Corrington is professor and former chairman of the Department of Zoology at the University of Miami, Coral Gables, Florida. He is a fellow of the American Association for the Advancement of Science and a member of several microscopist societies. For twenty-two years he wrote a column on microscopy in *Nature Magazine*.

Dr. Corrington is author of two other books, *Working with the Microscope* (McGraw-Hill, 1941) and *Adventures with the Microscope* (Bausch & Lomb, 1934). He is a contributing editor to *Bios,* quarterly journal of Beta Beta Beta, national honorary biological fraternity.